SEAR...

and
DISCOVER

by Claire Drury

Structured activities to develop information skills

Claire Drury manages the Learning Resources Centres at Failsworth School. She has worked closely with colleagues to develop an information skills programme which puts the LRC/library at the heart of the curriculum.

The projects in SEARCH and DISCOVER are based on this experience, have been thoroughly tried and tested and will enhance learning in many subject areas.

Summary of the Projects

Topic	Subject	Way of Working	Group	Outcome	Information Skills Focus
Healthy Eating	Food Technology / Science	Independently or in pairs	Y7, S1 (Ages 11-12)	Survey Letter to Problem Page	Using a range of resources. Finding specific information. Using information to draw conclusions.
Famous Scientists	Science	Pairs	Y7, S1 (Ages 11-12)	Balloon Debate	Locating information. Reading for information. Deciding which information is important. Presenting information persuasively.
THE ROMAN EMPIRE	History	Groups of four to six, with independent work as well	Y7, S1 (Ages 11-12)	Poster	Using a range of resources. Reading to find specific information. Organising and presenting information.
Shakespeare	English	Independently	Y8, S2 (Ages 12-13)	Booklet	Locating information. Reading to find specific information. Organising information.
Planets	Science	Pairs	Y8, S2 (Ages 12-13)	Holiday Brochure	Locating information. Reading to find specific information. Presenting factual knowledge imaginatively.
Earthquakes	Geography	Pairs with some independent work	Y8, S2 (Ages 12-13)	Board Game	Locating information. Reading for information. Note taking. Organising and presenting information creatively.
DEBATE	English	Groups of four initially and then into pairs	Y9, S3 (Ages 13-14)	Debate	Locating information. Reading for information. Note taking. Analysing and interpreting information. Presenting information persuasively.
Charities	RE / Citizenship / English	Independently or in pairs	Y9, S3 (Ages 13-14)	Choice of: Radio / TV appeal Interview Letter writing	Formulating research questions. Locating information. Reading and note-taking. Analysing and interpreting information. Presenting information in a variety of formats.

Contents

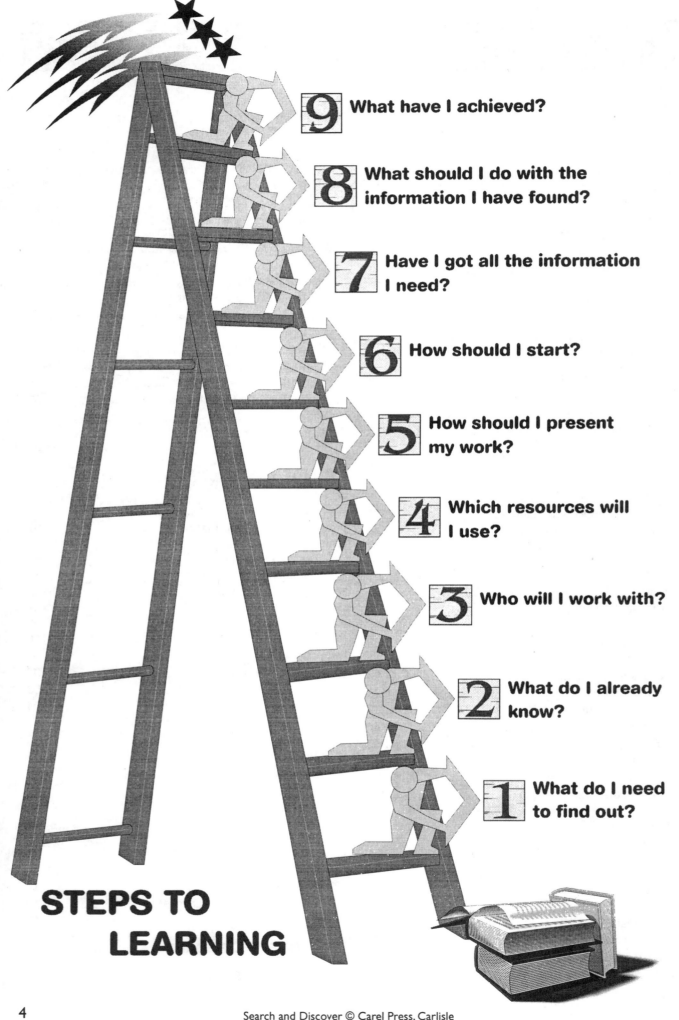

9 What have I achieved?

8 What should I do with the information I have found?

7 Have I got all the information I need?

6 How should I start?

5 How should I present my work?

4 Which resources will I use?

3 Who will I work with?

2 What do I already know?

1 What do I need to find out?

STEPS TO LEARNING

Introduction

The Library/LRC plays a vital role in helping students to develop information handling skills. This is most successful when information skills projects are embedded in the curriculum so that students undertake a purposeful piece of work with an added emphasis on actively finding, gathering, analysing, organising and presenting information.

Search and Discover
- includes eight separate projects, each designed to help students develop their information handling skills.
- places each project firmly within a curriculum area.
- shows how the library/LRC is central to learning and the curriculum.
- provides a structure for librarians and teachers to work in partnership.
- offers differentiated approaches to support the least able and stretch the most able.
- gives preparation notes for librarian and teacher to assist with planning and teaching.
- emphasises **Steps to Learning** as a common framework to encourage effective planning and help students navigate their way through tasks.
- emphasises the importance of existing knowledge as a foundation for further research.
- provides a varied range of student friendly outcomes which will motivate and encourage.
- shows students that information handling skills are transferable.

Search and Discover is about using your school library/LRC to promote and develop information handling skills. The eight projects cover a wide variety of subject areas, each with clear preparation notes to assist in planning and teaching.

There are no set rules to guarantee success, but here we offer some suggestions to help the projects run smoothly and to ensure that staff and students get the most out of the experience.

1 Work together
A partnership between teacher and librarian is essential for supporting students during information skills projects. The teacher will have an overview of the curriculum and the students, while the librarian can ensure successful use of resources and focus on the development of information handling skills. Initially, working in partnership may feel unfamiliar. The teacher may want to do a particular

project in the library but feel unsure about the resources available. The librarian may be keen to undertake a project on healthy eating, for example, but wonder which teacher to approach and how to organise it. **Search and Discover** provides a basis for discussion and planning, and a structure for you to use and adapt, making the co-operative process easier to initiate.

While students are using the library to undertake a piece of work linked to the curriculum, they must cope with working independently and also take greater responsibility for what and how they learn. This is likely to be more successful if the adults helping them are confident in their respective roles. Although we can't all be like Morecambe and Wise, a 'double act' is essential. Whichever project you decide on, it is essential to meet and plan the work.

Consider your respective roles and ensure the following are discussed:
- How will students work in the library/LRC? Do tables need to be moved to accommodate larger or smaller groups?
- How long will the work take? Each project is likely to require several library/LRC sessions.
- During the introductory lesson will the librarian talk to the whole class, for example about resources?
- How will the librarian work with students? Will it be with individuals who would particularly benefit, or with students working on CD Roms or the internet, or on an ad hoc basis as needs arise?
  - Students will be away from their familiar environment, but will classroom rules still apply? Is this feasible, especially if rules such as not being out of seat are normally upheld?
  - If students misbehave, should the librarian intervene, or always leave it to the teacher?
  - Will the librarian store students' work and encourage them to work in the library during their own time?
  - If homework is set, should some of the resources be kept for reference or overnight loan?

2 Be organised

All the projects in **Search and Discover** require that staff spend time on planning and organising. None are intended as quick fixes or time fillers.

The **Steps to Learning** (see p4) provide an identical framework for each project, assisting librarian and teacher during their planning and providing a structure to help students navigate their way through the tasks. The latter is especially important and the **Steps to Learning** reinforce the message that similar strategies can be adopted to find and use information regardless of the subject area.

The planning stage is an opportunity for teacher and librarian to familiarise themselves with the whole project and agree on any changes to be made. All the projects are flexible and you may wish to tailor certain aspects to your own needs.
Consider doing a project with different classes in the same year group. You will probably be investing considerable time, effort and, possibly, money, so the greater the number of students who benefit the better and, of course, any initial organisational problems are easier to iron out second, third and fourth time around.

3 Obtain plenty of resources

Sufficient resources are vital as nothing destroys a research project more quickly than having to share one book between four students. It may be possible to consult other agencies such as the Schools Library Service or the public library. If you are planning to do the same project with several classes and on a regular basis perhaps extra resources could be purchased.

The preparation notes will advise of any specific resources required. If you are collecting or sending away for resources try to allow plenty of time. Where possible we have named suitable websites and CD Roms, although of course new ones appear every day. Recommended book lists are not included as it would be impossible to guarantee an exhaustive and up to date list. It was also felt that such a list was unnecessary for projects being planned by librarians.

4 Never start a research project cold

Many of the projects are intended as ongoing rather than discrete units of work. All are linked closely to the National Curriculum so a project may begin in the classroom, continue in the library and conclude back in the classroom.

These projects aim to raise confidence and develop information handling skills alongside learning about the subject. Research is more likely to be successful if built on a firm foundation of knowledge, so asking a student who has never learnt anything about earthquakes to go and research them is akin to asking the average adult to research quantum physics. Therefore an important question in the **Steps to Learning** is 'What *do* I know already?' Students could be encouraged to begin the project by talking about what they have already learnt in the classroom. This will help them to feel confident about their own knowledge and their ability to build on it. If this stage is ignored, they may feel out of their depth when the research element begins and it will be much harder to keep them motivated and on task.

5 Go to town on the introduction

The majority of students appreciate encouragement and support when embarking on the challenges of a research project and this is emphasised through the introductory lesson.

> Friends, Romans, Students, lend me your ears ... is this a library that I see before me ...

This lesson is the perfect vehicle for teacher and librarian to share their objectives with students. Each of the **Steps to Learning** can act as a focus for discussion and explanation, time spent on this now will pay dividends as the project progresses. By the time students start their research they will have a clear idea of what they have to do, feel confident that tasks can be broken into manageable chunks and understand the outcome expected of them. The introductory lesson will be more successful if students can be shown an example of the outcome, perhaps one completed by another class or, if this is the first time you have done the project, you may have to make it yourself.

6 Assume nothing

Developing appropriate information skills is of equal importance to learning about a subject. Students will bring a variety of skills and experiences to their work; librarian and teacher must be able to meet their individual needs. This approach to learning can be a challenge for both staff and students. Staff are managing a large number of individuals of varying abilities, all working at their own pace and sometimes on different activities. Students are beginning to make decisions about their own learning and taking greater responsibility for planning and organising their work.

> Well, an encyclopedia is ...

Remember that we are expecting a great deal. This kind of work focuses on a variety of skills; students are encouraged to be methodical, organised, tenacious, motivated, independent and co-operative. In addition we are helping them to develop complex information handling skills. Every student is different. Some will never have seen an encyclopedia before, while others will be more advanced internet users than you are. Pitching your responses to their demands at exactly the right level is challenging, exhausting and hugely rewarding.

7 Encourage reading and stop copying

All the projects require students to find specific information so that they will be encouraged to read actively and avoid the temptation of copying, but that doesn't mean this will automatically happen.

> Miss, I've finished my project!

To encourage reading and stop copying, students must start with an essential question from the **Steps to Learning: What do I need to find out?** This will help them focus on the tasks ahead.

Once students have found the information they need the next step is to read. This can be one of the most important and demanding stages as, whichever resource they are using, whether book, pamphlet, internet or CD Rom, it is crucial that students engage with the text – reading, thinking and understanding. Many students hit a stumbling block at this point. Sometimes the reading stage doesn't happen at all and students simply pick up a pen and start copying. I remember one student's project which started with 'and...' because that was the first word on the page from which she copied.

Every student relates to text in a personal way and it can be difficult to identify a set procedure that should be followed by every person. Some students feel that reading is not a genuine learning activity and perhaps this is our fault because achievement is so often judged in terms of the written word. Others know they should 'write it in their own words' but are not sure how to do this, and feel so overwhelmed that the only option is to copy, perhaps changing the occasional word here and there.

There are strategies that can be adopted to promote active reading and writing skills and it can be helpful to share these with students, even explaining your concerns to ensure they understand the importance of active reading and writing.

Introduce the ten-minute rule. Once information has been located, students spend at least ten minutes reading before they begin to write. This can work even if specific information requiring a brief answer is needed – in this case students could be encouraged to read around the information they are looking for. Part of the ten-minute rule could include reading the synopsis, and then scanning the contents of a book to obtain an overview.

Highlight Text. When using CD or internet printouts encourage students to read once for an overview, followed by a second reading armed with a pen to highlight or underline important information. When using a book suggest that during the second reading students pick out five important pieces of information from a page of text. 'Post-it' notes can be useful, especially for older or more able students who want to jot down a few notes relating to a particular page.

Use spider diagram and notes grids. These can help students to avoid copying large chunks of information. Proformas of each are included on p118 and many of the projects include them.

Introduce writing frameworks. Many of the projects in **Search and Discover** offer writing frameworks to help students turn the information they have found into a different genre such as an interview, a brochure or a persuasive presentation. The writing framework offers a skeleton of basic phrases in a sequence which encourages logical

and coherent writing. Students respond positively to the assistance provided by writing frameworks and students of all abilities often produce work of an impressive quality. Two excellent books on writing frameworks by David Wray and Maureen Lewis are listed on p120.

Well, it's not exactly a free lesson ...

8 Be visible

These projects aim to promote the skills of independent learning and it can be tempting to set students off on project work and then leave them to get on with it. However, this may cause problems, especially when students drift off task or go off at a tangent. To prevent this the teacher or librarian could draw the class together occasionally, perhaps to review ongoing work or to emphasise a particular issue or problem. This is especially helpful for less able students. The **Steps to Learning** could be used as a structure so that the class is brought together at the beginning and end of each step to provide support and build confidence.

It is vital to achieve balance. Students should know that help is available, while not expecting to be spoon-fed. The presence of at least two adults is a huge advantage – it can reduce the time students need to wait for help and make it easier to maintain an atmosphere of purposeful industry.

Finally, relax and enjoy it.

Things won't always go according to plan, especially when you are starting a project for the first time. That doesn't matter as the opportunities should far outweigh any teething problems. Remember, when the library is teeming with activity as thirty plus students actively research and study, this is independent learning at its best.

Healthy Eating - Preparation Notes

Subject: **Food Technology / Science**

Topic: **Healthy Eating**
Students work independently or in pairs to research nutrients, junk food and healthy eating.

Group: **Y7, S1**

Emphasis: **Curriculum**
Develop knowledge of nutrients and understanding of the importance of a healthy diet.

Information Skills
Using a range of resources.
Finding specific information.
Using information to draw conclusions.

Personal Development
Co-operation and teamwork.
Increased confidence in using own knowledge.

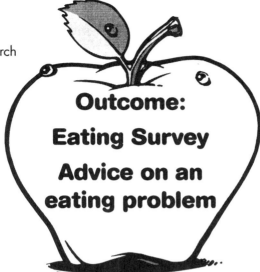

Outcome:

Eating Survey

Advice on an eating problem

Resources Provided

Steps to Learning, p4
The **STEPS TO LEARNING** are a series of questions designed to help students plan their research and navigate their way through a project or task. The steps provide a consistent framework for all the projects in this book.

Nutrients, p11
Students use a variety of resources to research nutrients, finding out why they are important and which foods contain them.

The Big Fight: Healthy Eating v Junk Food, p12
Students use a variety of resources to find out about junk food and healthy eating.

Snack Time Survey, p13-14
Students conduct a survey to establish peoples' favourite junk food snacks and healthy snacks. They analyse the results of their survey and think up alternatives to the junk food snacks.

Problem Eating? & Problem Solved, p15-16
Enables students to pull together everything they have learnt, explaining why junk food is unhealthy and giving healthier alternatives.

Resources Required

The Library/LRC

Dictionaries

Books on food, diet and health

Encyclopedias, Internet and CD Roms

Food Packaging

This topic aims to introduce a variety of resources including books, students' own knowledge, teacher's knowledge, other people's opinions (established through a survey) and food packaging. In that sense the topic could be done in the classroom, but giving the project a firm library base will help students to see that their library or LRC is one of a number of vital resources.

Healthy Eating - Organisation and Planning

Pre Lesson

- Decide how class will work – either independently or in pairs.
- Obtain and organise resources – food packaging to demonstrate the variety of nutrients in different foods as well as in 'junk food'. You will specifically need packaging from beefburgers, pizzas and chocolate bars. Brochures on healthy eating (often found in supermarkets) would also be useful. The International Food Information Council have an interesting web site at: ificinfo.health.org/brochure/10tipkid.htm

Lesson 1 Introduction

In Library/LRC or classroom

Focus on steps to learning:

1 What do I need to find out?

Brief explanation of this project and how it fits into past and future learning.

2 What do I already know?

Emphasise that an important resource is students' own knowledge of nutrients and of junk food. One way to build confidence is to do a class brainstorm, e.g. asking them to name different nutrients.

3 Who will I work with?

Opportunity to set out parameters. You may have decided that students will work independently for certain parts, such as **NUTRIENTS** and in pairs for other aspects such as the **SNACK TIME SURVEY.**

4 Which resources will I use?

Class brainstorm all the possible resources which could be used to find out about food.

5 How should I present my work?

Brief explanation of the **SNACK TIME SURVEY** and **PROBLEM EATING?** so that students know where they are heading. Not too much detail is needed at this stage as students need to complete **NUTRIENTS** and **THE BIG FIGHT** first.

6 How should I start?

Explain **NUTRIENTS** in more detail, emphasising the variety of resources to be used. To ensure students sample all types of resources you could set up library tables as work stations: books on one, packaging on another and CD Roms set up on computers etc. Divide the class into groups, circulating them every ten minutes or so. Following on from **NUTRIENTS**, students need to work on **THE BIG FIGHT** which will help them to understand the health problems of junk food.

Lesson 2 onwards

In Library/LRC continuing research.

7 Have I got the information I need?

Begin the lesson by revising what has been learnt so far. This could be done as a class question and answer session to tease out students' understanding of junk food and healthy eating.

8 What should I do with the information?

The next step is to conduct the **SNACK TIME SURVEY** and to respond to the letter on **PROBLEM EATING?** Begin with the survey. Students either survey members of their class or family and friends (an ideal homework). Collating and analysing the results of their survey is important and the **SNACK TIME SURVEY** is intended to help them do this. This topic culminates with the problem page letter, **PROBLEM EATING?**. Students should be encouraged to use their notes from **NUTRIENTS** and **THE BIG FIGHT** to help them write their letter in response to this. **PROBLEM SOLVED** is a writing framework, which may be helpful to those who find it difficult to organise their ideas.

9 What have I achieved?

Students should feel a sense of achievement in being able to offer an informed opinion. Encourage them to fill in the SELF EVALUATION sheet, page 117, to think about these.

What Next?

- Create a class display using the **SNACK TIME SURVEY**.
- Design posters to encourage healthy snacks – these could be displayed in the school canteen.
- Organise a meeting with catering staff so that students can discuss how menus are planned and how students can be encouraged to eat healthier snacks.
- Use the research to plan a healthy lunch box, possibly for a younger age group.

HEALTHY EATING - NUTRIENTS

Examples of food which are rich in ...	Why it is important to the body
PROTEIN	
CARBOHYDRATES	
FAT	
VITAMINS	
MINERALS	
FIBRE	

HEALTHY EATING - THE BIG FIGHT
Healthy Eating v Junk Food

Find out what we mean by junk food. Write the meaning down here.

Find out what we mean by healthy eating. Write the meaning down here.

Look at the food packaging and find out:

How much salt is there in a beefburger? Beefburger: salt per 100g =

How much sugar is there in a chocolate bar? Chocolate: sugar per 100g =

How much fat is there in a pizza? Pizza: fat per 100g =

Find out what health problems arise from eating:

Too much salt

Too much sugar

Too much fat

HEALTHY EATING - SNACK TIME SURVEY
Healthy Food or Junk Food

Brainstorm with a partner and think of 10 examples of snack foods.
Try to think of 5 healthy snacks and 5 junk food snacks.

Now you are going to do a survey to find out what other people eat as snacks. You are going to survey 20 people – in your class or family or friends.

Write down the 10 snacks you thought of in the left hand column of the table below.

Ask each of your 20 people to look at the list of snacks and say which ones they have eaten during the last week. Use a tally chart to show the number.

Name of Snack	Number

HEALTHY EATING - SNACK TIME SURVEY
Healthy Food or Junk Food

Now analyse your survey results:

Which was the most popular junk food snack? _____

Which was the least popular junk food snack? _____

Which was the most popular healthy snack? _____

Which was the least popular healthy snack? _____

Overall which is more popular - junk food snacks or healthy snacks? _____

Can you give a reason for this? _____

_____

Now list all the junk foods from your survey in the table below.

For each type of junk food snack can you think of a healthier alternative which has less sugar, fat and salt? One has been done for you as an example.

Junk food	Does this food have a lot of:			Healthier alternative
	Sugar	Salt	Fat	
Fizzy cola	✔			Fresh orange juice
1				
2				
3				
4				
5				

You have learnt about healthy eating and junk food. Now you are going to use what you have learnt to write an important letter. Ask you teacher or librarian for **PROBLEM EATING?**

Search and Discover © Carel Press, Carlisle

HEALTHY EATING - PROBLEM EATING?

Read this letter sent to a problem page in a teenage magazine.

Dear Annabelle,

I hope you don't think my problem is silly.

I love going to McDonalds and Burger King! I go at least three times a week. My favourite is Chicken McNuggets with a large fries and coke.

Now my Mum and Dad have told me I'm not allowed to eat this kind of food anymore. They say this kind of food is bad for me. Can you tell me why it is bad for me? Also what can I eat if I can't eat burgers or chicken nuggets or fries?

I am only a bit overweight and I think that I am quite healthy. I go swimming twice a week and I am on the school netball team. I would really like to be involved in sport when I grow up, perhaps as a PE teacher.

Yours hungrily,

Kate Aziz

Use the notes you have made to write a reply to this letter.

Tell Kate why junk food is bad for her.

Give her some ideas about healthier alternatives.

Try to write persuasively.

HEALTHY EATING - PROBLEM SOLVED

Dear Kate,

Eating junk food is bad for you for several reasons.
One reason is...

Another reason is...

A further reason is...

It is important to eat a healthy diet. The human body needs lots of nutrients including...

Nutrients are important to the body for many reasons. One reason is...

A further reason might be...

There are several healthy snacks you could eat instead of junk food. These include...

Finally I would like to remind you that...

Yours,

Annabelle

Famous Scientists – Preparation Notes

Subject: Science

Topic: **Famous Scientists and Inventors**
Students work in pairs to research famous scientists or inventors then, as a full group, hold a balloon debate to decide which scientist is the most important.

Group: **Y7, S1**

Emphasis: **Curriculum**
Develop understanding of scientific inventions or discoveries.

Information Skills
Locating information.
Reading for information.
Deciding which information is important.
Presenting information persuasively.

Personal Development
Decision making.
Developing a line of argument.
Persuading others.

Outcome: Balloon debate

Resources Provided

Steps to Learning, P4
The **STEPS TO LEARNING** are a series of questions designed to help students plan their research and navigate their way through a project or task. The steps provide a consistent framework for all the projects in this book.

Balloon Debate, p19
This explanation sheet can be used for reference, possibly enlarged as a poster.

Scientists and Inventors, p20-21
The list of names is not meant to be prescriptive. It is drawn from experience about available materials. It was particularly disappointing not to find appropriate materials about more women scientists. Encourage less able students to select names for whom suitable materials are available. The practice passages about John Logie Baird can be used to emphasise the skill of reading to obtain information. The second version is modified to be easier to read.

Fact File, p22
Three fact files will be required for most pairs. The least able may only complete one or two.

The Most Important Scientist ..., p23
Encourages students to develop their research and analytical skills by deciding why each scientist should stay in the balloon or be thrown out. One copy of this will be needed for each pair. This stage may be omitted by the least able students.

Keep them in the Balloon!, p24
This writing framework helps students to articulate the reasons why their scientist is the most important. It forms the basis for their speech in the balloon debate.

Voting Sheet, p25
Students record votes in each heat and the final outcome. The *ACTIVE LISTENING* sheet (page 119) will be useful here.

Resources Required

The Library/LRC

A wide variety of books on scientists/famous people

Encyclopedias (text and electronic)

Famous Scientists- Organisation and Planning

Pre Lesson

- Divide class into pairs.
- Obtain and organise resources.

Lesson 1 Introduction
In Library/LRC or classroom.

Focus on steps to learning:

1 What do I need to find out?

Brief explanation of this project and how it fits in to past and future learning.

2 What do I already know?

Before being given the list, students brainstorm the names of any famous scientists and inventors and their discoveries.

3 Who will I work with?

Opportunity to set out parameters and emphasise team work.

4 Which resources will I use?

Discuss available resources. Test students' understanding of biography. Discuss the importance of finding out about the person as well as their invention or discovery. Advice about using encyclopedias may be useful here, especially for younger secondary students.

5 How should I present my work?

Explain the idea of the balloon debate. Go through the steps they will take to get there: researching three scientists, deciding for themselves who is the most important and presenting their case to the rest of the class. **The Balloon Debate** sheet on page 19 can be issued to students or displayed to remind them of the process.

6 How should I start?

Before any decisions can be made, students have to do the research and that means reading about their scientists and writing key facts about them. Practise as a class using the passages about **John Logie Baird** on page 21. (Two versions are provided to allow for different abilities). Emphasise the importance of reading to obtain information. Following this, students can start their research.

Lesson 2 onwards
In Library/LRC continue research and prepare for debate.

7 Have I got the information I need?

Ensure **Fact Files** are completed (three for most pairs) and ask students to use **The Most Important Scientist...** to help them decide. Emphasise that partners must agree and must be able to give reasons for their choice. You could save time for the least able by allowing them to go straight from the **Fact File** to **Keep them in the Balloon!** (page 24)

8 What should I do with the information?

To assist with their presentation, students may wish to conduct additional research on their chosen scientist. Students may also wish to design a poster with suitable headlines which could be displayed during their presentations. The writing framework **Keep them in the Balloon!** on page 24 is intended as an outline to help them construct a persuasive presentation.

There are several ways to organise the debate. If time is pressing you may wish to stop after the heats, allowing a number of scientists equal importance. Alternatively, if several classes are doing the same project, a grand final could involve all of them, perhaps (if you're feeling brave) during an assembly.

9 What have I achieved?

The Balloon debate itself is a visible indication to students of what they have achieved. The active voting sheet, **Balloon Debate Voting Sheet,** page 25, will help them decide who should remain in the balloon and some positive feedback on strengths and weaknesses of their presentations will also be helpful, The *ACTIVE LISTENING* sheet (page 119) will be particularly useful here.

What Next?

- Students use their **Fact Files** to create a passport for their most important scientist. These are used for display purposes.

- Students design a chat show interview to find out about their scientists and what makes them tick. This could be written and then recorded or acted.

- Students design an A4 poster about their most important scientist, including biographical information, the five most important facts, a picture or diagram of their discovery or invention. The posters are then designed as a classroom timeline. This will help students to see the context of scientific discovery.

- Students use the timeline to debate which is the most important invention or discovery in a century.

BALLOON DEBATE

Imagine that many famous scientists and inventors are packed into a hot air balloon.

The balloon is losing height and to stop it crashing people will have to be thrown out.

You and your partner will find out about some of these scientists, decide which one you think should stay in the balloon and give a talk to the rest of your class to persuade them.

People will vote for the scientist they think should stay in the balloon and the scientist who wins the most votes will be saved.

Name	Invention/Discovery
Charles Babbage	Father of the computer
Alexander Graham Bell	Telephone
Karl Benz	Built first motor car
Marie Curie	Radium
Charles Darwin	Theory of evolution
Michael Faraday	Electric motor
Alexander Fleming	Penicillin
Benjamin Franklin	Lightning conductor
Galileo Galilei	Telescope
Edward Jenner	Smallpox vaccination
James Joule	Discoveries about energy
Joseph Lister	Antiseptics
Isaac Newton	Theory of gravity
Florence Nightingale	Development of nursing techniques
Alfred Nobel	Dynamite
Louis Pasteur	Pasteurisation
George Stephenson	First public railway
Patrick Steptoe	In vitro fertilisation (test tube babies)
Alessandro Volta	Battery
Orville & Wilbur Wright	Powered flight (aeroplanes)

John Logie Baird

John Logie Baird was born in Scotland in 1888. He studied electrical engineering in Glasgow. He started work as an engineer but did not like it so, at the age of 26 he left work to become an inventor.

At first he made no money from his inventions.

In 1906 he began work on a machine that could transmit pictures as well as sound. He called it 'seeing by wireless' but we know it as television. In 1923 he took out a patent on his invention. In 1924, he managed to send a picture of an object from a wireless transmitter to a receiver a few feet away in his laboratory. The next year he managed to send pictures of recognisable human faces.

In 1926 he showed his invention to the public at the Royal Institution of Great Britain, in London. This was the first real television broadcast. In 1928 he sent pictures across the Atlantic for the first time. In 1931 he made the first outside broadcast, it was of the famous horse-race, the Derby.

When the BBC began to broadcast television as a public service in 1936, they used Baird's system and a rival one invented by Marconi. Eventually they decided to use the Marconi system, partly because it used a cathode ray tube and partly because the cameras were smaller and easier to use inside a studio. The Marconi system is still in use today.

Just before World War 2, Baird gave a demonstration of colour television. In 1944 he showed facsimile television, the forerunner of Ceefax, and just before he died in 1946 he was working on stereoscopic television, which gives a 3-D image.

Some of his other inventions include: fibre optics, radar (even before it was developed by Robert Watson-Watt), early video recording (on wax records and steel discs) and a 'noctovision' system using infra-red rays to see at night.

John Logie Baird

John Logie Baird was born in Scotland in 1888. He started work as an engineer but at the age of 26 he left work to become an inventor.

At first he made no money with his inventions.

In 1906 he began work on what we now know as television. He called it 'seeing by wireless'. In 1924, he managed to send a picture of an object to a receiver a few feet away. The next year he was able to send pictures of human faces.

In 1926 he showed his invention to the public. This was the first real television broadcast. In 1928 he sent pictures across the Atlantic for the first time. In 1931 he made the first outside broadcast, it was of the famous horse-race, the Derby.

BBC television began in 1936. At first, they used Baird's system and one invented by Marconi. In the end, they decided to use the Marconi system which is still used today.

Just before World War 2, Baird invented colour television. In 1944 he showed an early version of Ceefax. He died in 1946.

Some of his other inventions include: fibre optics, radar, early video recording and a system using infra-red rays to see at night.

FACT FILE

Your names _____ & _____

Name of Scientist / Inventor _____

Famous for: Inventing... ☐   Discovering... ☐   Developing... ☐

The invention, discovery or development was _____

This is some information about the life of this person:

Born: Died

Nationality

Two reasons why this invention/discovery/development is important to us now:

One reason why we would be worse off without this invention/discovery/development:

Inventions, discoveries and developments often involve the work of lots of people. These are the names of other scientists connected with this:

_____   _____

More information about the scientist and the invention/discovery/development:

Your names _____ & _____

Name: Famous for:

Reason to stay in the balloon:

Reason to be thrown out of the balloon:

Name: Famous for:

Reason to stay in the balloon:

Reason to be thrown out of the balloon:

Name: Famous for:

Reason to stay in the balloon:

Reason to be thrown out of the balloon:

DECISION TIME!

Decide with your partner which scientist or inventor should stay in the balloon. You must both agree and be sure of your decision, because you are now going to persuade the rest of the class that the scientist / inventor you have chosen is the most important of all time!.

Now ask for the next sheet: KEEP THEM IN THE BALLOON!

KEEP THEM IN THE BALLOON!

Names _____ & _____

We think the most important scientist / inventor is...

This person should stay in the balloon for several reasons. One reason is...

Another reason might be...

A further reason might be...

This person has improved our lives in several ways. One way is that...

This has resulted in...

To finish this presentation I would like to remind you that...

Balloon Debate Voting Sheet

The heats

Heat 1: 1st four teams

	in balloon	out of balloon
Name of scientist _____	☐	☐
Name of scientist _____	☐	☐
Name of scientist _____	☐	☐
Name of scientist _____	☐	☐

Heat 2: 2nd four teams

	in balloon	out of balloon
Name of scientist _____	☐	☐
Name of scientist _____	☐	☐
Name of scientist _____	☐	☐
Name of scientist _____	☐	☐

Heat 3: 3rd four teams

	in balloon	out of balloon
Name of scientist _____	☐	☐
Name of scientist _____	☐	☐
Name of scientist _____	☐	☐
Name of scientist _____	☐	☐

Heat 4: 4th four teams

	in balloon	out of balloon
Name of scientist _____	☐	☐
Name of scientist _____	☐	☐
Name of scientist _____	☐	☐
Name of scientist _____	☐	☐

The Final

	in balloon	out of balloon
Name of scientist _____	☐	☐
Name of scientist _____	☐	☐
Name of scientist _____	☐	☐
Name of scientist _____	☐	☐

Winner _____

THE ROMAN EMPIRE – PREPARATION NOTES

Subject: **History**

Topic: **The Roman Empire**
Students work in six groups of four or five, each taking at least one, and possibly two, questions within the research area. They should also be encouraged to produce their own questions and find answers. The six areas of research are: Entertainment, Slavery, Growing Up, Transport, Families and Homes, Sanitation

Group: **Y7, S1**

Emphasis: **Curriculum**
Develop understanding of Roman life.

Information Skills
Using a range of resources.
Reading to find specific information.
Organising and presenting information.

Personal Development
Improved co-operation, teamwork and organisational skills.

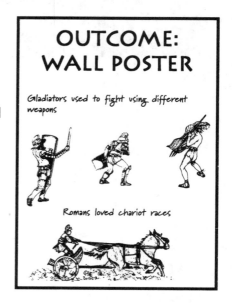

OUTCOME: WALL POSTER

Gladiators used to fight using different weapons

Romans loved chariot races

Resources Provided

Steps to Learning, p4
The **STEPS TO LEARNING** are a series of questions designed to help students plan their research and navigate their way through a project or task. The steps provide a consistent framework for all the projects in this book.

Six Project Planners, p31-32, 38, 43, 47, 54, 59
Each planner has an identical format and an identical first page (see page 31) but the research questions on the reverse are different for each topic. Occasionally a question will appear in more than one topic. This serves to show the links between the topic areas.

Support Material
Some questions have a ✔ next to them, indicating that supporting resource sheets are available. This does not always mean that they are suitable for lower ability students, however, the following questions are particularly suitable for the less able:

Entertainment:	Application Form: Gladiator, p34
	Types of gladiator, p37
Slavery:	Runaway Slave, p41
Growing Up:	The Rome Grammaticus: Special punishment report, p45
Transport:	Building a road (Two versions, multiple choice is easier), p48-49
Families and Homes:	Roman houses: The rich and the poor, p55
Sanitation:	Keeping clean, p62

Resources Required

The library/LRC
A wide variety of books about the Roman Empire
Encyclopedias (text and electronic)
An atlas
A comprehensive, encyclopedic dictionary

THE ROMAN EMPIRE – ORGANISATION AND PLANNING

Pre Lesson

- Divide class into six groups, each with four or more students.

- Obtain and organise resources. The following electronic resource may prove useful: http://members.aol.com/Donnclass/Romelife.html, although this is largely a text based web site, a wealth of information, relevant to the topics is on offer.

  An excellent CD Rom called The Romans is available from Anglia Multimedia, 2nd Floor, Rouen House, Rouen Road, Norwich NR1 1RB (01603 760000). With a little preparation, its use could be built into the research topics. Caesar 3 (from Sierra, see www.sierra-online.co.uk) is an educational game requiring students to build a Roman town. Perfect as an extension activity or during a lunchtime session in the library/LRC.

Lesson 1
In Library/LRC or classroom

- Focus on **STEPS TO LEARNING** in the project planner (see page 28-29 for ideas).

- By the end of this lesson, everyone should have chosen which questions to tackle. If time allows, students could begin reading. This may be an opportunity to introduce the 10 minute rule (see page 8).

- Some of the research questions ask students to imagine themselves as a Roman. To help them get into character, a list of Roman names is included on page 30 as part of the glossary.

Lesson 2 onwards
In Library/LRC continuing research.

Once the research stage is complete, students need to collate all their work and display it on a poster.

As you near this stage, emphasise the importance of best work and the need for clear titles and headings. Ensure everyone's work is included.

What next?

Ideas for extending the work.

If some groups finish earlier:

- Top Five Facts – Each member of the group decides on the most interesting fact, one member collates these for display on the poster.

- Students can create a glossary for their area of research (see page 30 for suggested keywords).

- Students can list additional questions, inspired by their research, which you can use with the next class.

- Prepare a quiz, puzzle sheet, wordsearch or similar which other students can answer from careful study of their poster.

- Fill in a *SELF EVALUATION* sheet (page 117).

When all groups are finished:

- Swap wall posters with another group and using the information, create a fact sheet about the topic suitable for the rest of the class.

- Run their own Eurovision Poster Contest – display the finished posters and mark each others, awarding points for clarity, presentation etc.

- In groups, present their wall poster to the rest of the class and explain the information on it.

USING THE ROMAN EMPIRE PROJECT PLANNER

The front of the project planner is used by all the students. The reverse varies, depending on the topic.

The Project Planner is divided into broad areas, each beginning with a question, the answer to which assists in the research process.

Write all the topics on the board. Check students understand what each means.
Extension Idea: Class discussion about what we already know about each topic.

Students write down names and initials now.
Extension Idea: Class discussion on advantages and disadvantages of working in a group.

Discuss available resources. Confirm that students understand what the following are for:
keywords, index, glossary, contents.
Extension Idea: Groups look at the books and practise the above skills, eg
'If you were researching Growing up in Roman Times, what alternative keywords might you look up?'
'How many of you can find the word slavery in the index?'

THE ROMAN EMPIRE PROJECT PLANNER

Which topic am I researching?

The name of your topic is _____

Who will I work with?

Your class will be divided into groups and each group will research a different topic.

Write down the names and initials of the people in your group. Put your name first:

Name	Initials	Name	Initials

Which resources will I use?

During your research you will use lots of different resources including:

non fiction books   **encyclopedias**   **computer information**

How will I present my work?

Everyone in your group will work together to produce a wall poster all about your topic.

Later on, you may give a talk to the rest of your class, explaining the information on your wall poster.

How should I start?

A good way to start your research is to ask questions and then look for the answers.

Over the page are questions to get you started.

You should discuss with your group who is going to work on each question.

Write that person's initials next to the question.

Turn over the page to find your questions.

Search and Discover © Carel Press, Carlisle   31

Emphasise the importance of starting research with a question.
Extension Idea: Offer some examples:
'What's on at the cinema?'
'How many planets are there in the solar system?'
Discuss how you would go about finding the answers to these questions.

Before starting work it helps to know what the finished product will look like. Have an example to show them if possible.
Extension Idea: Have 6 genuine examples, one for each group to look at. Group discussion on the good qualities of each and areas for improvement.

Students need to read through the questions and decide in their group which they are going to tackle.

Save this until you have gone through the entire project planner with them, as this activity will lead naturally into the next lesson and the start of their research.

There is a space for students to formulate their own research question.

Indicates a question which has a supporting worksheet. This could take a variety of forms, such as a map or diagram, a writing framework, or a fact sheet. The worksheets are intended to support both research and presentation. Sometimes these supporting materials are specifically designed for the less able and this is indicated in the preparation notes. At other times, students may wish to tackle the question without using the support materials – preferring to research and present information in their own way.

ROMAN ENTERTAINMENT

		Support Sheets	Initials
1	Imagine you are a gladiator and describe one of your fights. Don't forget to explain who (or what) you are fighting and what sort of weapons you use.	✔	
2	Fill in the job application form for the post of gladiator. Use the information you have found to make up a good candidate for this job.	✔	
3	Fill in the fact file about the Roman Colosseum.	✔	
4	Imagine you are a Roman journalist. Write a report about a chariot race you have been to see.	✔	
5	Try to find pictures of each of these gladiators: Murmillo Samnite Thracian Retiarius Describe the armour and weapons each of them have.	✔	
6	What was a Roman theatre like? What kind of plays did they watch?		
7	Write a list showing the types of entertainment enjoyed by Romans and by people today. Can you see any similarities?		
8	Romans used the baths to keep clean but they also used them for other activities. Find out what sort of things they did.		
9	Write your own question here		

Have I got the information I need?

Tick the boxes when your group have done each of the following.

We have used a variety of resources including: Books ☐   Computers ☐   Encyclopedias ☐

We have answered all the questions ☐   All the work is our best work ☐

We have read our work and it makes sense to us. ☐

Well done!

What should I do with the information I have found?   Now you can make your poster.

What have I achieved?

- You have learned about **Roman Entertainment**
- You have found information   • You have selected the information you need
- You have created a display of that information

Now you need to check all the information on your poster and discuss with the teacher and librarian what to do next.

32   Search and Discover © Carel Press, Carlisle

This checklist reminds students of the need to check that they have completed all the tasks and encourages them to take some responsibility for their own work.

Extension Idea: Class discussion on why this question is important.

You should emphasise the importance of this question and ask pupils if they can think of any other achievements (ie worked well with the group, got better at using computers etc). They can record anything that they are particularly pleased with on the SELF EVALUATION sheet (page 117).

Extension Idea: Decide how you are going to use the finished wall posters (see 'What Next?') and give students a taste of how the project might develop when they return to the classroom.

Glossary

Entertainment:
Amphitheatre
Circus
Ludi
Thumbs up
Thumbs down
Colosseum
Gladiator
Chariot race
Trident

Growing up:
Bulla
Papyrus
Grammaticus
Wax Tablet
Stylus
Astronomy
Paterfamilias
Pedagogus
Abacus

Families and Homes:
Domus
Fresco
Insulae
Lararium
Mosaic
Paterfamilias
Atrium
Hypocaust
Toga
Pestle and Mortar

Slavery:
Spartacus
Denarius
Freed Man
Auction
Fugitivarii

Transport:
Groma
Viaduct
Galley
Pax Romana
Legion
Mediterranean
Denarius
Roman Empire
Milestone
Cursus Publicus

Sanitation:
Strigil
Aqueduct
Hypocaust
Tepidarium
Caldarium
Frigidarium
Massage
Olive oil
Gymnasium

Some Roman Names:

GIRLS	BOYS
Antonia	Antonius
Augusta	Caius
Claudia	Claudius
Cornelia	Julius
Flavia	Marcus
Helena	Marius
Julia	Petronius
Livia	Quentus
Octavia	Sestius

Search and Discover © Carel Press, Carlisle

THE ROMAN EMPIRE PROJECT PLANNER

Which topic am I researching?

The name of your topic is _____

Who will I work with?

Your class will be divided into groups and each group will research a different topic.

Write down the names and initials of the people in your group. Put your name first:

Name	Initials	Name	Initials

Which resources will I use?

During your research you will use lots of different resources including:

non fiction books   **encyclopedias**   **computer information**

Roman Entertainment

Gladiators used to fight using different weapons

Romans loved chariot races

How will I present my work?

Everyone in your group will work together to produce a wall poster all about your topic.

Later on, you may give a talk to the rest of your class, explaining the information on your wall poster.

How should I start?

A good way to start your research is to ask questions and then look for the answers.

Over the page are questions to get you started.

You should discuss with your group who is going to work on each question.

Write that person's initials next to the question.

Turn over the page to find your questions.

ROMAN ENTERTAINMENT

		Support Sheets	Initials
1	Imagine you are a gladiator and describe one of your fights. Don't forget to explain who (or what) you are fighting and what sort of weapons you use.	✔	
2	Fill in the job application form for the post of gladiator. Use the information you have found to make up a good candidate for this job.	✔	
3	Fill in the fact file about the Roman Colosseum.	✔	
4	Imagine you are a Roman journalist. Write a report about a chariot race you have been to see.	✔	
5	Try to find pictures of each of these gladiators: Murmillo Samnite Thracian Retiarius Describe the armour and weapons each of them have.	✔	
6	What was a Roman theatre like? What kind of plays did they watch?		
7	Write a list showing the types of entertainment enjoyed by Romans and by people today. Can you see any similarities?		
8	Romans used the baths to keep clean but they also used them for other activities. Find out what sort of things they did.		
9	Write your own question here		

Have I got the information I need?

Tick the boxes when your group has done each of the following.

We have used a variety of resources including: Books ☐   Computers ☐   Encyclopedias ☐

We have answered all the questions ☐   All the work is our best work ☐

We have read our work and it makes sense to us. ☐

Well done!

What should I do with the information I have found?   Now you can make your poster.

What have I achieved?

- You have learned about **Roman Entertainment**
- You have found information   • You have selected the information you need
- You have created a display of that information

Now you need to check all the information on your poster and discuss with the teacher and librarian what to do next.

Search and Discover © Carel Press, Carlisle

THE GLADIATOR FIGHT

My name is _____ and I am a gladiator.

To prepare for a fight I ...

Keywords

armour   net
weapons   shield
dagger   helmet

Today I am fighting against ...

Murmillo   Samnite
Thracian   Retiarius
wild animals

The fight begins and all around me ...

audience
Emperor
cheering
excitement
shouting

The fight is going well when all of a sudden ...

injury   death
blood   sweat
fear   defeat
winner

Finally, at the end of the fight ...

Mercury   Pluto
thumbs up
thumbs down
Emperor
dead bodies

APPLICATION FORM
GLADIATOR

NAME _____ AGE _____

HEIGHT _____ WEIGHT _____

RELIGION _____

GIVE THREE THINGS YOU WOULD ENJOY ABOUT THE JOB OF GLADIATOR.

1 _____

2 _____

3 _____

GIVE THREE REASONS WHY YOU WOULD MAKE A GOOD GLADIATOR.

1 _____

2 _____

3 _____

IF YOU ARE MORTALLY WOUNDED IN A FIGHT, DO YOU HAVE ANY FINAL REQUESTS?

APPLICATION APPROVED BY _____*Claudius Maximus*_____

IN CHARGE OF GLADIATOR TRAINING

THE ROMAN COLOSSEUM
FACT FILE

Date built: _____   Where it is: _____

What it is made of: _____

Shape: _____

Why it is called the Colosseum: _____

_____

Its real name: _____

What it was used for in Roman times: _____

_____

_____

_____

How many people could sit in it: _____

Why people still want to visit it today:

1 _____

2 _____

CHARIOT RACE

Welcome to the Circus Maximus where we have an exciting chariot race for you to watch.

My name is _____ and I am your commentator.

We have four teams competing today, these are

_____   _____   _____   _____

Just in case you have never been to a chariot race before, let me describe what the chariot looks like _____

_____

Today the favourites to win are _____ because _____

_____

The race has begun and _____ are in the lead with the

_____ close behind. It's going to be an exciting race.

This is the _____ lap so there is only one lap to go.

Oh no! We have a disaster. This is what has happened (make this up based on

what you know) _____

_____

_____

And _____ are the winners!

Type of Gladiator: _____

Strengths: _____

_____

Weaknesses: _____

_____

Type of Gladiator: _____

Strengths: _____

_____

Weaknesses: _____

_____

Type of Gladiator: _____

Strengths: _____

_____

Weaknesses: _____

_____

Type of Gladiator: _____

Strengths: _____

_____

Weaknesses: _____

_____

ROMAN SLAVERY

		Support Sheets	Initials
1	Make a list of the jobs carried out by slaves from Greece, slaves who worked on farms and slaves owned by the government.	✔	
2	Imagine you are captured and become a Roman slave. Describe what happens at the slave auction where you are to be sold.	✔	
3	Complete a poster offering a reward for a runaway slave.	✔	
4	Imagine you are a rich Roman citizen in need of a slave. What kind of slave do you need? Make a list of all the jobs your slave could do.	✔	
5	Find out how Roman slaves could become free.		
6	Find out how Roman slaves were identified.		
7	Some slaves were badly treated. Can you find out how they were punished and what happened to them?		
8	Who was Spartacus? What did he do to help Roman slaves?		
9	Write your own question here		

Have I got the information I need?

Tick the boxes when your group has done each of the following.

We have used a variety of resources including: Books ☐   Computers ☐   Encyclopedias ☐

We have answered all the questions   ☐   All the work is our best work ☐

We have read our work and it makes sense to us. ☐

Well done!

What should I do with the information I have found?   Now you can make your poster.

What have I achieved?

- You have learned about **Roman Slavery**
- You have found information
- You have selected the information you need
- You have created a display of that information

Now you need to check all the information on your poster and discuss with the teacher and librarian what to do next.

THE JOBS OF ROMAN SLAVES

Slaves from Greece did
these jobs

1 _____

2 _____

3 _____

Slaves who worked on farms
did these jobs

1 _____

2 _____

3 _____

Slaves who worked for the
government did these jobs

1 _____

2 _____

3 _____

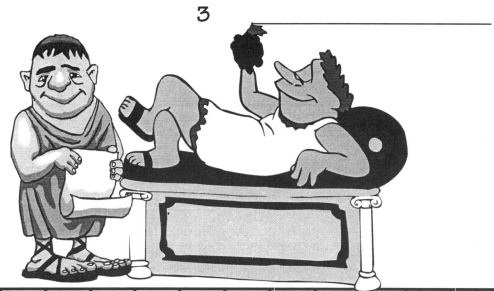

THE SLAVE AUCTION

My name is _____ and I have been captured.

I come from _____ . I think I am going to be made into a
Roman slave.

I am with lots of other people including ...

Keywords

friends

children

market place

rich

I stand at the auction and look around me. I see ...

poor

fear

anger

gladiator

teacher

fit

The auctioneer begins telling the audience about us. He says ...

intelligent

pretty

handsome

ugly

weak

The person next to me is sold to ...

citizen

farmer

slave

Now it is my turn. The auctioneer describes me. He says ...

I can't believe it. I have been bought by...

Now finally, I go off to start my new life.

Runaway Slave

Have you seen this slave?

Name _____   Age   _____

Hair Colour _____   Height   _____

Country the slave came from _____

This slave is good at _____

And   _____

Reward _____

If anyone has any information about this slave please tell

_____

Who lives at _____

_____

THE SLAVE OWNER

My name is _____. I am a rich Roman citizen. I have just visited the auction and bought a new slave.

These are some of the jobs my slave will do.

To help me the slave will:

1 _____

2 _____

3 _____

To help my wife the slave will:

1 _____

2 _____

3 _____

To help my children the slave will:

1 _____

2 _____

3 _____

When we have a party the slave will:

1 _____

2 _____

3 _____

The slave ought to be grateful. I won't beat him very often and this is better than being a gladiator!

Search and Discover © Carel Press, Carlisle

GROWING UP IN ROMAN TIMES

		Support Sheets	Initials
1	Use the chart to compare your school with a Roman school.	✔	
2	Imagine you are a Roman teacher. Fill in the report about a naughty pupil.	✔	
3	You are a 14 year old Roman boy who is about to become an adult. Describe what happens at the special ceremony.	✔	
4	Find out what happened to celebrate the birth of a baby in Roman times.		
5	Write down the Roman Numerals for 1 to 10. Now find the numerals for 50, 100, 500 and 1000. Can you write today's date in numerals?		
6	Find the Roman alphabet and write down the letters. Can you write a sentence using the Roman alphabet? Which letters do we have which the Romans did not?		
7	Roman children did not have exercise books and pens. Find out what they used instead.		
8	Find out what kind of games and toys Roman children enjoyed. Make a list of as many as you can find.		
9	Write your own question here		

Have I got the information I need?

Tick the boxes when your group has done each of the following.

We have used a variety of resources including:　　Books ☐　　Computers ☐　　Encyclopedias ☐

We have answered all the questions ☐　　　　All the work is our best work ☐

We have read our work and it makes sense to us. ☐

Well done!

What should I do with the information I have found?　Now you can make your poster.

What have I achieved?

- You have learned about **Growing up in Roman times**
- You have found information
- You have selected the information you need
- You have created a display of that information

Now you need to check all the information on your poster and discuss with the teacher and librarian what to do next.

SCHOOL COMPARISON

COMPARE THE ROMAN SCHOOL WITH YOUR SCHOOL

	THE ROMAN SCHOOL	MY SCHOOL
What subjects do the children study?		
What time does the school day begin?		
What time does the school day end?		
How many days a week do children go to school?		
How old are children when they start primary school?		
How old are children when they leave primary school?		
Do girls and boys go to secondary school?		

THE ROME GRAMMATICUS

SPECIAL PUNISHMENT REPORT

NAME OF PUPIL: _____

REASON FOR REPORT: _____

_____

PUNISHMENT GIVEN: _____

_____

SIGNED _____
                            (Teacher)

SPECIAL PUNISHMENT REPORT

NAME OF PUPIL: _____

REASON FOR REPORT: _____

_____

PUNISHMENT GIVEN: _____

_____

SIGNED _____
                            (Teacher)

BECOMING AN ADULT

My name is _____. I am fourteen years old and today is the ceremony when I become a man.

Keywords

First of all my parents give me...

toga
adult
childhood
bulla
temple
gods
sacrifice
offerings
feast

Then I get rid of...

Afterwards, we visit the....

Finally we...

ROMAN TRANSPORT

		Support Sheets	Initials
1	Find out how a Roman road was built. Use the information you find to fill in the sheet.	✔	
2	Look at the pictures of the different types of transport. Name them and explain what each was used for.	✔	
3	Why do you think the Mediterranean Sea was so important to trade in Roman times? The questions on the map of the Roman Empire will help you to find out.	✔	
4	Each of these words is to do with transport. Find out what they mean.	✔	
5	Many important goods were shipped to Rome from distant lands. Look at the list of goods and find out which country each came from. Mark this information on the map.	✔	
6	Wine and olive oil were difficult to transport. Why do you think this was? How did the Romans manage to transport wine and olive oil?		
7	Produce two spider-diagrams to show different types of transport in Roman times and today. Describe some of the differences.		
8	Find out about Pax Romana. How did this help Roman travellers?		
9	Write your own question here		

Have I got the information I need?

Tick the boxes when your group has done each of the following.

We have used a variety of resources including: Books ☐ Computers ☐ Encyclopedias ☐

We have answered all the questions ☐ All the work is our best work ☐

We have read our work and it makes sense to us. ☐

Well done!

What should I do with the information I have found? Now you can make your poster.

What have I achieved?

- You have learned about **Roman Transport**
- You have found information
- You have selected the information you need
- You have created a display of that information

Now you need to check all the information on your poster and discuss with the teacher and librarian what to do next.

BUILDING A ROAD

When they were _____ a road, the Romans looked for the

shortest, _____, flattest route. To find this they took sights

from one _____ point to another. They probably did this by

lighting _____, flares or beacons, observing carrier

_____, or using a **groma** .

Once the route had been planned, the turf and _____ were

cleared. Then a trench was dug about 1m _____. It was filled

with _____ of stone.

The _____ of the road had a raised curve called a camber.

_____ were made at the side of the road to drain the water

away. This stopped puddles forming, which would have _____

the road if they had frozen.

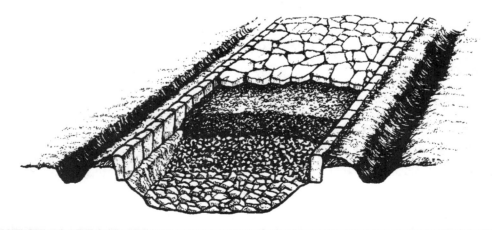

BUILDING A ROAD

Use your sources to find the correct words.
Cross out the incorrect words.

1   When they were planning a road, the Romans looked for a short, straight   curved   zig-zag   flat route.

2   To find this they took sights from one   high   low   decimal   point to another.

3   Once the road was planned, the turf and   people   trees   hills were cleared. Then a trench was dug about 1m   wide   deep   high.

4   It was filled with   lines   statues   layers   of stone.

5   The surface of the road had a raised   stone   roof   curve   called a camber.

6   The Romans put   rivers   ditches   pipes   at the side of the road to drain the   oil   water   stones   away. This   helped   showed   stopped   puddles forming, which would have   helped   destroyed   cracked   the road if they had frozen.

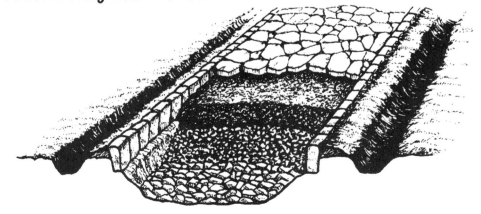

ROMAN TRANSPORT

Type of Transport:

_____

What it was
used for:

_____

_____

Type of Transport:

_____

What it was
used for:

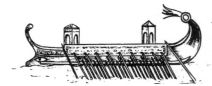

_____

_____

Type of Transport:

_____

What it was
used for:

_____

_____

Type of Transport:

_____

What it was
used for:

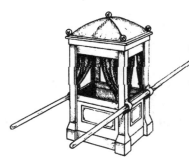

_____

_____

Type of Transport:

_____

What it was
used for:

_____

_____

Type of Transport:

_____

What it was
used for:

_____

_____

Type of Transport:

_____

What it was
used for:

_____

_____

Search and Discover © Carel Press, Carlisle

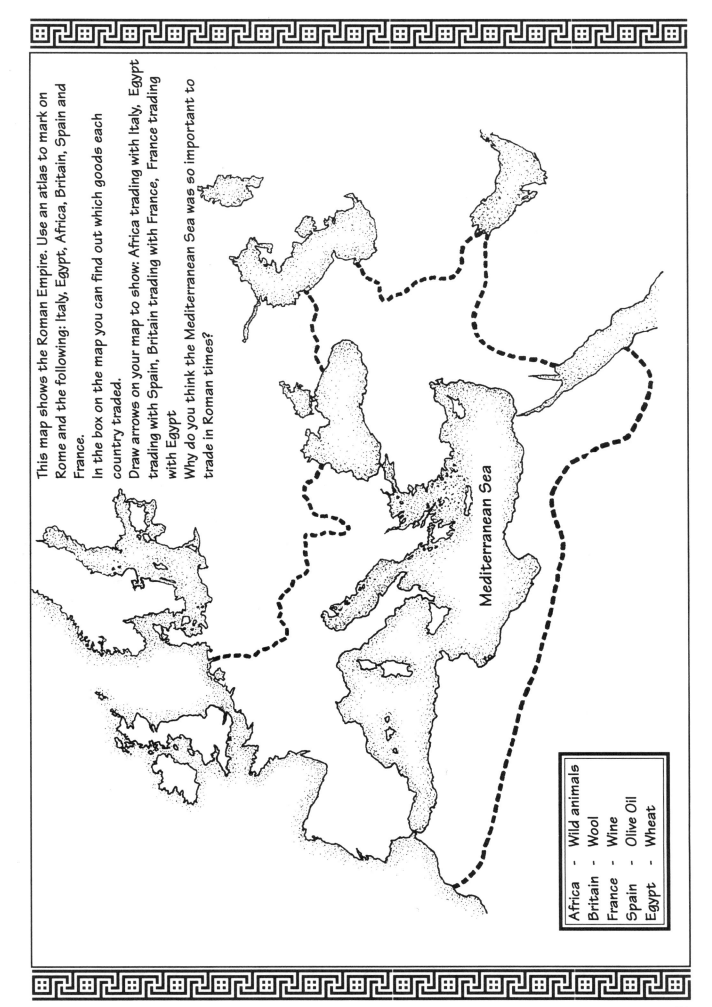

This map shows the Roman Empire. Use an atlas to mark on Rome and the following: Italy, Egypt, Africa, Britain, Spain and France.

In the box on the map you can find out which goods each country traded.

Draw arrows on your map to show: Africa trading with Italy, Egypt trading with Spain, Britain trading with France, France trading with Egypt

Why do you think the Mediterranean Sea was so important to trade in Roman times?

Mediterranean Sea

Africa	-	Wild animals
Britain	-	Wool
France	-	Wine
Spain	-	Olive Oil
Egypt	-	Wheat

ROMAN TRANSPORT

The following words are all to do with transport:

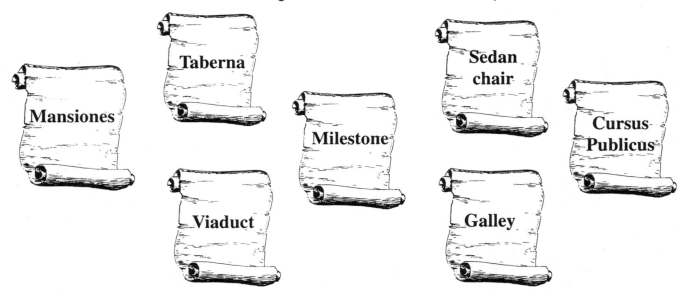

Mansiones

Taberna

Milestone

Sedan chair

Cursus Publicus

Viaduct

Galley

Can you match the words with their meanings and perhaps find an illustration?

A stone marking each mile along a route

Guest houses where travellers could stay. They were built every 15 miles along important Roman roads. Some were very large, but they were not always comfortable

A Roman warship with three levels of oars

A bridge to carry a road across a river or valley. Often built using a series of arches

A public house where Roman travellers could get food, drink and rest

A postal service which collected and delivered important messages for the government

A method of transport for rich Roman citizens. It was usually carried by slaves

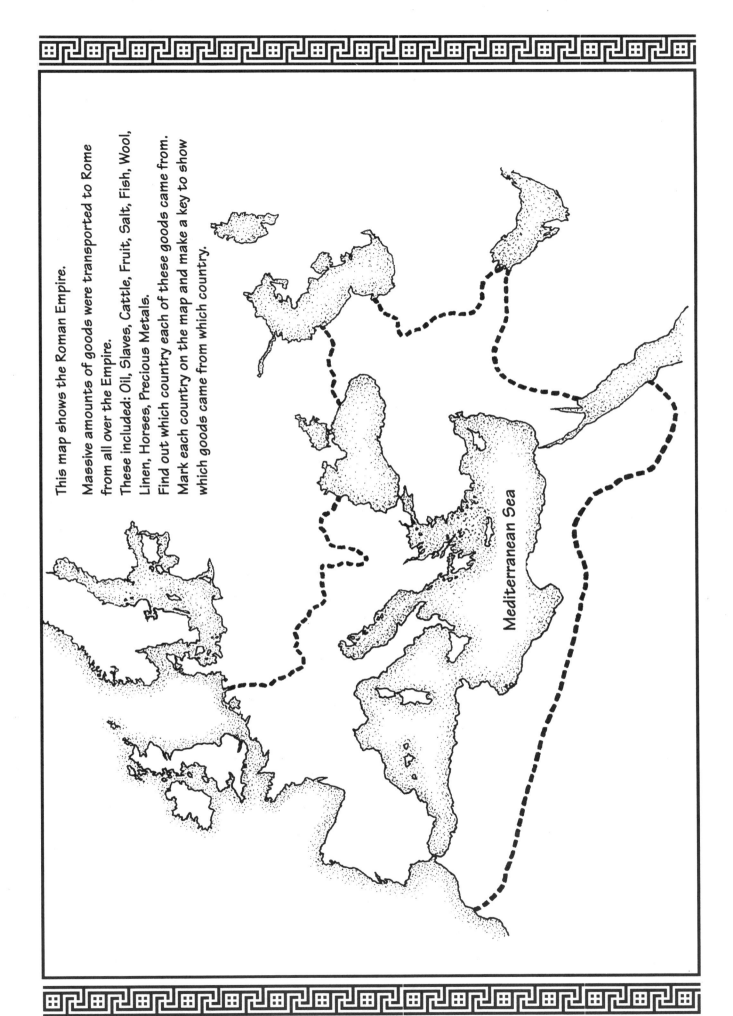

This map shows the Roman Empire.

Massive amounts of goods were transported to Rome from all over the Empire.

These included: Oil, Slaves, Cattle, Fruit, Salt, Fish, Wool, Linen, Horses, Precious Metals.

Find out which country each of these goods came from.

Mark each country on the map and make a key to show which goods came from which country.

Mediterranean Sea

ROMAN FAMILIES & HOMES

		Support Sheets	Initials
1	Use the information in the books to fill in the gaps on the chart which compares rich and poor Roman homes.	✔	
2	Use the information in your sources to match the Roman people with their jobs.	✔	
3	Find out what each room in a Roman house was used for.	✔	
4	What was a mosaic used for? Design your own mosaic for a Roman villa.	✔	
5	What sort of clothes did men and women wear in Roman times? Find out about their hair styles and jewellery too. Illustrate your information with pictures.		
6	Find out about Roman central heating. Draw and label a diagram to explain how Roman central heating worked.		
7	Make a list of the household gods. Write down what each was worshipped for.		
8	Imagine you are a chef in Roman times. Design a menu for a Roman banquet.		
9	Write your own question here		

Have I got the information I need?

Tick the boxes when your group has done each of the following.

We have used a variety of resources including: Books ☐   Computers ☐   Encyclopedias ☐

We have answered all the questions ☐   All the work is our best work ☐

We have read our work and it makes sense to us. ☐

Well done!

What should I do with the information I have found?   Now you can make your poster.

What have I achieved?

- You have learned about **Roman Families and Homes**
- You have found information
- You have selected the information you need
- You have created a display of that information

Now you need to check all the information on your poster and discuss with the teacher and librarian what to do next.

ROMAN HOUSES
THE RICH AND THE POOR

Can you fill in the gaps on the chart? The first one has been done for you.

	RICH	POOR
Name of house	Domus or villa	Insulae
Number of rooms		
Do you have a garden?		
Are you allowed to cook inside the house?		
Do you have a bathroom?		
Do you have running water?		
Do you have servants?		
Do you have central heating?		

Here is my drawing of a Roman house

ROMAN PEOPLE

A government official in charge of markets, streets and public buildings. He also organised the public games.	
A person with no freedom. These people were forced to work and sometimes treated cruelly.	
The most important government official. In charge of the Roman senate and the army.	
The supreme ruler of the Roman empire.	
A fighter employed to entertain people, often a slave.	
The poorest Roman citizen	
One of the people who governed Rome.	
An important Roman citizen who belonged to a noble family.	

Can you match these Roman people with the description of their job?

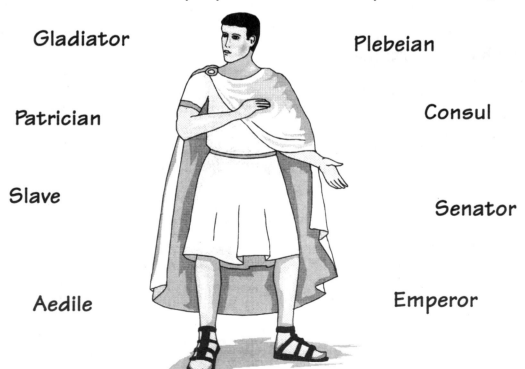

Gladiator

Plebeian

Patrician

Consul

Slave

Senator

Aedile

Emperor

ROMAN HOUSES

A Roman villa, owned by a rich Roman citizen usually had several rooms.

These are the Roman names for the rooms. Can you find out what the names are in English? The first one has been done for you.

Atrium = Hall   Impluvium =

Cubiculum =   Tablinum =

Triclinium =   Peristyle =

Lararium =

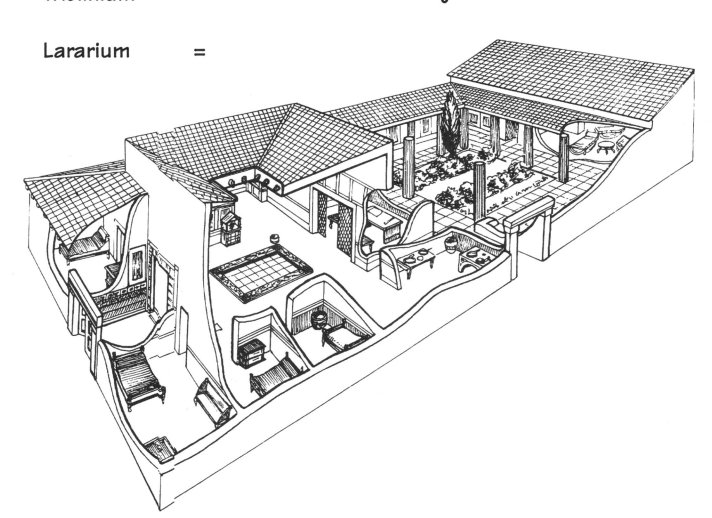

Roman Mosaics

A mosaic is

decoration
floor
rich
pictures

The Romans used mosaics because

Another reason for this might be

This is how the Romans laid a mosaic.
First of all

designer
artist
plan
tiles
stone
brick
small
plaster

Secondly

Thirdly

The artists often made mosaic pictures. These pictures often showed

and

Here is my example of a mosaic

ROMAN SANITATION

		Support Sheets	Initials
1	Imagine you are an important and rich Roman citizen and describe your visit to the baths.	✔	
2	Look at the plan of the bath house. Use the information in your sources to label the plan.	✔	
3	Compare the way we keep clean with the way the Romans kept clean.	✔	
4	Imagine you are the rich owner of a Roman bath house. Write out a list of jobs which a slave would do to help you.	✔	
5	Imagine you are a Roman tour guide. Explain what the Roman toilets looked like and how they worked.		
6	Draw a picture of a strigil and explain what it was used for.		
7	Find out how the Romans heated the water for the baths. (Clue: a keyword is Hypocaust.) Draw a diagram to show how it worked.		
8	Find out what an aqueduct was used for.		
9	Write your own question here		

Have I got the information I need?

Tick the boxes when your group has done each of the following.

We have used a variety of resources including: Books ☐   Computers ☐   Encyclopedias ☐

We have answered all the questions ☐   All the work is our best work ☐

We have read our work and it makes sense to us. ☐

Well done!

What should I do with the information I have found?   Now you can make your poster.

What have I achieved?

- You have learned about **Roman Sanitation**
- You have found information
- You have selected the information you need
- You have created a display of that information

Now you need to check all the information on your poster and discuss with the teacher and librarian what to do next.

Visit to the Baths

My name is _____. I am a Roman citizen and today I am visiting the baths.

First of all I

```
┌─────────────────────────────────────────────────┐
│                                                 │
└─────────────────────────────────────────────────┘
```

I am going to use three baths during my visit. This is what they are like

```
┌─────────────────────────────────────────────────┐
│                                                 │
│                                                 │
│                                                 │
│                                                 │
│                                                 │
└─────────────────────────────────────────────────┘
```

Now I have finished bathing I dry myself.
There are all sorts of things I could do next including...

```
┌─────────────────────────────────────────────────┐
│                                                 │
│                                                 │
└─────────────────────────────────────────────────┘
```

I love visiting the baths because

```
┌─────────────────────────────────────────────────┐
│                                                 │
└─────────────────────────────────────────────────┘
```

another reason is

```
┌─────────────────────────────────────────────────┐
│                                                 │
└─────────────────────────────────────────────────┘
```

Now it is time to go home to my wife and family. I wonder what the slave will have cooked for dinner. I hope it is honeyed dormice!

Search and Discover © Carel Press, Carlisle

A ROMAN BATH HOUSE

Label this drawing

KEEPING CLEAN

	IN ROMAN TIMES	TODAY
What do you use to get clean?		
Where does the water come from?		
How big is the bath?		
How many people share a bath?		
How often do you have a bath?		

BATH HOUSE SLAVE

My name is _____

I am a rich Roman citizen and I own a large bath house.
I am looking for a new slave to help me look after the bath house.

These are the jobs the slave will do to look after my customers who come in to use the baths.

1 _____

2 _____

3 _____

4 _____

These are the jobs the slave will do to look after the baths

1 _____

2 _____

3 _____

4 _____

Shakespeare – Preparation Notes

Subject: **English**

Topic: **Shakespeare's life and works**
In each section all students should be able to tackle the first page which deals with the most basic facts, most should manage the second which adds detail to their knowledge. The third part of each section is more challenging, less explicit in its questioning and demands wider reading and interpretation. This should be seen as extension work for the more able.

Group: **Y8/9, S2/S3**

Emphasis: **Curriculum**
Gives a useful background to the study of a Shakespeare play

Information Skills
Locating information.
Reading to find specific information.
Organising information.

Personal Development
Organising time and information.

Resources Provided

Steps to Learning, p4
The **STEPS TO LEARNING** are a series of questions designed to help students plan their research and navigate their way through a project or task. The steps provide a consistent framework for all the projects in this book.

Who was Shakespeare? 1-3, p66-68
This section deals with the basic facts of Shakespeare's family life, working life and home. The second sheet concentrates on significant dates in Shakespeare's working life. There is room here for interpretation and students should be encouraged to add other important events.

Shakespeare's plays 1-3, p69-71
This deals with definitions, a close look at the play the students are likely to be studying and a look at how Shakespeare's phrases are a part of our language. The third activity, *Famous sayings*, is possible using a dictionary of quotations, but it is less time-consuming and more fun if a CD Rom or the Internet is used for the search.

Shakespeare's Theatre 1-3, p72-74
This looks at: The Globe, the work of a player and some of the conventions of Elizabethan theatre.

Resources Required

The library/LRC

A wide variety of books/electronic resources on Shakespeare, including copies of Carel Press' Shorter Shakespeare series

Access to the internet

Shakespeare – Organisation and Planning

Pre Lesson

- Divide the class into three groups. Each group to work on a different area of study. Within each group students can work independently.
- Obtain and organise resources. There is a wealth of material available on Shakespeare, including some excellent websites and video resources. Books suitable for all levels of ability are also readily available.

The following electronic resources will prove useful: Shakespeare's complete works can be found at the-tech.mit.edu/Shakespeare
and
www.gh.cs.usyd.edu.au/~matty/Shakespeare
These sites are useful for checking quotations and finding references.

William Shakespeare: The complete Works on CD ROM: (Andromeda Interactive for Mac & PC) is fun and also allows for a variety of searches, for example by imagery.

www.learnfree.co.uk contains an entertaining and educational section 'talking to Shakespeare' in which you can ask a direct question to 'William Shakespeare'. The answers, provided by academics writing in role, are informative, age appropriate and very lively, but take a few days.

Surfing with the bard: www.ulen.com/shakespeare has useful and enthusiastic sites for teachers and students and a discussion room, as well as relevant links.

www. shakespeare.org.uk is the site of the Shakespeare Birthplace Trust and contains lots of background information about Shakespeare and Stratford.

Videos relevant to Shakespeare and to English Literature in general are available from:
Trumedia Ltd, PO Box 374, Headington, Oxford, OX3 7NT, Tel: 01865 763097

Lesson 1
In Library/LRC or Classroom.

Focus on steps to learning:

1 What do I need to find out?

Brief explanation of this project and how it fits in to past and future learning.

2 What do I already know?

Class brainstorm anything they already know about Shakespeare. It may be a surprising amount. Write down the responses on a flip chart or large piece of paper and keep this to return to later.

3 Who will I work with?

Explain that although they will be working on the same topic and at the same time as other people, what they produce will essentially be their own booklet as background reference for their study of Shakespeare.

4 Which resources will I use?

Discuss available resources. Test students' understanding of the term 'biography'. Discuss the importance of finding out about Shakespeare's work as well as his life. Emphasise the importance of reading and remind students about the ten-minute rule (See Introduction page 8).

5 How should I present my work?

Explain that the resource pages they will be given will form the basis of a booklet but that they can add extra pages themselves if there are areas which they wish to develop more fully.

6 How should I start?

By the end of the project, all the groups should have covered all three areas of study. Explain that different groups will have different starting points:

Group 1 *Who was Shakespeare?*
Group 2 *Shakespeare's Plays*
Group 3 *Shakespeare's Theatre*

Lesson 2 onwards
In Library/LRC continue research and complete booklet.

7 Have I got the information I need?

Students should aim to complete the first sheet of each section quite quickly. Most students should be able to complete two sheets per session. Some will manage all three. The sheets are arranged in order of difficulty with sheet three in each area being significantly more difficult to research than the other two.

8 What should I do with the information?

The sheets here will build up into a background booklet but students may also wish to add their own information and illustrations. They will need to make a cover for their booklet but this can be done in the classroom at the end of the project or as a homework task.

9 What have I achieved?

The booklet itself shows students what they have achieved. The booklets can be displayed and students given a chance to look at each other's work. A satisfying finish can involve returning to the brainstorm sheet and adding to the knowledge they had at the beginning.

What Next?

- Students use their booklets to create a multiple choice quiz for use with their own class or with others.
- Students improvise a chat show interview with Shakespeare.
- Students design a display for the classroom or library/LRC in which they present the most important facts, quotations etc to a younger group.

Who was Shakespeare?

Basic Facts

EARLY LIFE

Date of birth _____

Place of birth_____

Father's name and occupation _____

Mother's name and occupation _____

Names of brothers and sisters_____

_____

MARRIED LIFE

Name of Wife

_____

Date of Marriage

_____

Name of 1st Child

_____

Born_____

Name of 2nd Child

_____

Born_____

Name of 3rd Child

_____

Born_____

WORKING LIFE

Title of first play _____

_____

_____

Date written or first performed

_____

Title of last play_____

_____

_____

Date written or first performed

_____

DIED Date_____

Buried in _____

Who was Shakespeare?

Shakespeare's Working Life

These are the dates of some important events in Shakespeare's working life. Some of them were also very important for all the other people in the country at that time.

Write down what you can find out about what happened at these times – the pictures give you some clues.

 *1585 -1592*

 *1594-1608*

1603

1599-1613

His home town

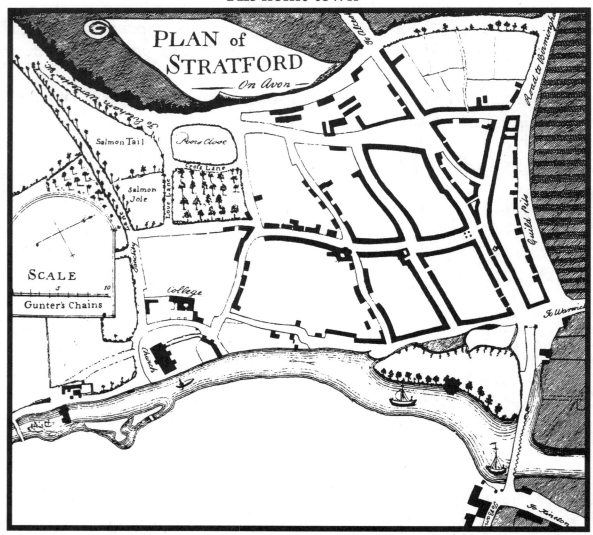

This map of Stratford upon Avon was drawn in 1759. The town had probably not changed very much since Shakespeare's day. It was kindly provided by the Shakespeare Birthplace Trust and can be seen in full on their website at www. shakespeare.org.uk

Mark these places on the map and explain why they were important to Shakespeare.

1   Mary Arden's house

_____

2   New Place

_____

3   The place where he went to school

_____

4   Henley Street

_____

5   Holy Trinity Church

_____

Shakespeare's Plays
What did he write?

Find a list of Shakespeare's plays. How many did he write? _____

Many lists divide the plays into **tragedies, comedies, history plays** and, sometimes, **romances.** Romances were also called **tragicomedies.**

A **Tragedy** is

A Tragedy by Shakespeare:

A **Comedy** is

A Comedy by Shakespeare:

A **History** is

A History play by Shakespeare:

A **Romance** is

A Romance by Shakespeare:

The Shakespeare play we will be/have been studying is

_____

It is a _____

Shakespeare's Plays

A close look at one play

Title of play

Type (tragedy etc)   Date written/performed

Place where the play starts

Other places where things happen

MAIN MALE CHARACTERS

Name   Brief description

1 _____   _____

2 _____   _____

3 _____   _____

MAIN FEMALE CHARACTERS

Name   Brief description

1 _____   _____

2 _____   _____

3 _____   _____

WHAT THE PLAY IS ABOUT

Shakespeare's Plays

Famous sayings

Some of Shakespeare's words are so famous that they have become part of our language.

Find out who said these famous words:

PHRASE	PLAY	SAID BY ...
Eaten me out of house and home	Henry IV	_____
Green-eyed monster	Othello	_____
I have not slept one wink	Cymbeline	_____
In my mind's eye	Hamlet	_____
My own flesh and blood	The Merchant of Venice	_____
Neither here nor there	Othello	_____

These phrases are also very well known. Find out which play they come from.

A horse! A horse! My Kingdom for a horse!   _____

Alas poor Yorick! I knew him, Horatio   _____

All the world's a stage   _____

Now is the winter of our discontent   _____

Parting is such sweet sorrow   _____

The quality of mercy is not strained   _____

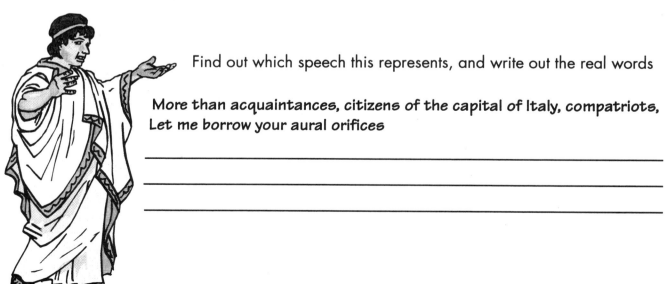

Find out which speech this represents, and write out the real words

More than acquaintances, citizens of the capital of Italy, compatriots, Let me borrow your aural orifices

_____

_____

_____

Shakespeare's Theatre

The Globe Theatre

Find out about the Globe (and other theatres) in Shakespeare's time.

What sort of people went to the theatre?

What did it cost?

What sort of props and costumes were used?

Was there any lighting or any special effects?

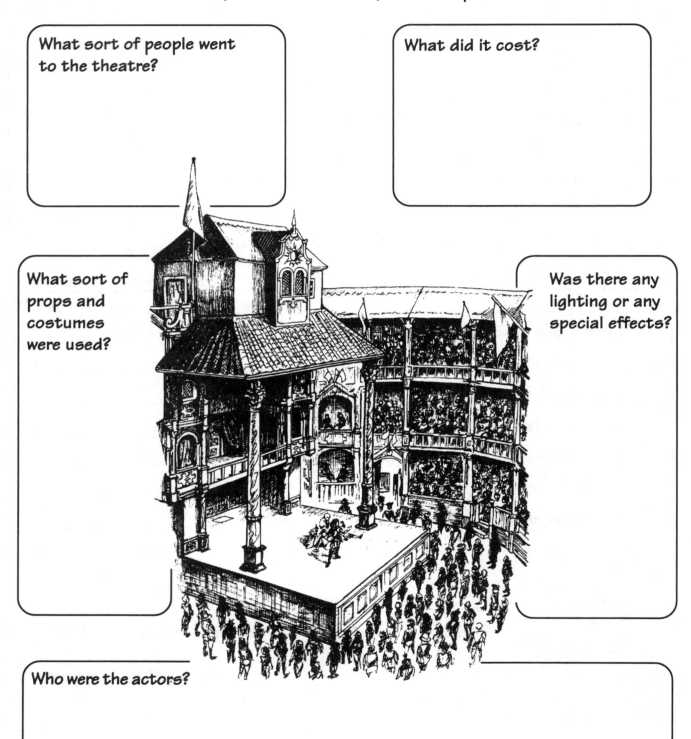

Who were the actors?

What other entertainments were on offer?

Search and Discover © Carel Press, Carlisle

Shakespeare's Theatre

A Player's View

My name is _____

and I am a player at the _____
playhouse.

I belong to the _____
company

When I stand on the stage
and look out I see

number of
people

seats

groundlings

lords and
ladies

One of my favourite plays is
_____ because

language

costumes

props

comedy

tragedy

Some people want to close our theatre because

crowds

sin

wickedness

disease

Shakespeare's Theatre

True or False

Find out whether the statements below are TRUE or FALSE – then give your opinion on them.

ABOUT THE THEATRE IN SHAKESPEARE'S TIME	T/F	OPINION
Only men could act on the stage		
All the audience had to keep quiet		
Only rich people could go to the plays		
Eating and drinking were banned		
They used trap doors and different levels on the stage		
A playhouse was a small house for children		
Some people wanted to ban plays		
They did not use costumes		
They did use props		
The people playing comic roles could make up extra bits		
There were very few theatres		
The plays were always staged at night		
Queen Elizabeth hated plays		
A player was another name for a musician		
Most of the playhouses were round		
The audience for a play would be about 20 people		

The Planets – Preparation Notes

Subject: **Science**

Topic: **The Planets**
Students work in pairs to design a holiday brochure for a planet.

Group: **Y8, S2**

Emphasis: **Curriculum**
Develop understanding of the planets in our solar system.

Information Skills
Locating information.
Reading to find specific information.
Presenting factual knowledge imaginatively.

Personal Development
Team work.

Resources Provided

Steps to Learning, p4
The **STEPS TO LEARNING** are a series of questions designed to help students plan their research and navigate their way through a project or task. The steps provide a consistent framework for all the projects in this book.

The Planet Fact File, p77
The comparative Planet Fact File will help students understand the similarities and differences between Earth and the planet they are researching. It also demonstrates that research is an essential stage in the project, hence the holiday brochure design is not the first activity.

For some students you may wish to provide a partially completed sheet and for all students it is essential to have had some explanation of mass and gravity.

Holiday Brochure, p78-79
For lower ability students, pages 78 and 79 provide a structure to use. Students need to use the information from their Planet Fact Files coupled with their imagination and this is often a challenge for lower ability students. They may, for example, need help in deciding on the advantages of a different length of day or year. These sheets will assist the student to follow a logical plan when designing the holiday brochure.

Resources Required

The Library/LRC

A wide variety of books on planets

Examples of holiday brochures – particularly the layout and type of language used

Encyclopedias (text and electronic)

Posters (There are some excellent Planets and Solar System posters available.)

The Planets – Organisation and Planning

Pre Lesson

- Divide class into pairs.
- Decide which planet each pair will research. You to decide? Students to decide?

Lesson 1 Introduction

In Library/LRC. Start of research.

Focus on steps to learning:

1 What do I need to find out?

Brief explanation of this project and how it fits in to past and future learning.

2 What do I already know?

Class discussion/brainstorm on what they have already learnt or already know. Many students already have an interest in this subject.

3 Who will I work with?

Opportunity to set out parameters and emphasise team work.

4 Which resources will I use?

Discuss available resources. Holiday brochures deserve a special mention.

5 How should I present my work?

If possible show a finished product. Ask for comments. Discuss good and bad points.

6 How should I start?

Show and explain Fact File. Draw attention to any areas where you think students may struggle. Emphasise that the information in the Fact File will be essential in their Holiday Brochure and therefore should not be rushed. Work as a team with lower ability and bring them together frequently to discuss findings and help keep them on task.

Lesson 2 onwards

In Library/LRC continuing research and designing holiday brochure.

7 Have I got the information I need?

Ensure Fact File is completed and remind them that the information here will be used in their holiday brochure. Some students view this as a completely separate piece of work and feel they are almost starting again, hence step 8!

8 What should I do with the information?

Hold a class discussion to decide what should be included in the holiday brochure. Less able students can be supported by using pages 78 to 79. To complete the sentences and do the illustrations on page 79 they need to use their imaginations. An illustration for Mars, for example, might show visitors enjoying a trip to an extinct volcano or sliding down a dry river canyon. The words and phrases at the end of page 79 are to assist them in writing a persuasive final sentence. Able students may want to build up a checklist of items for inclusion in their brochure, for example: vital equipment, where to stay etc.

9 What have I achieved?

Help students to analyse their success by offering them the SELF EVALUATION sheet on page 117. Help students to see that they have successfully undertaken research and redrafted their initial notes and ideas (i.e. the Fact File) into something far more substantial.

What Next?

- Students swap holiday brochures and use the information on each others to write a letter / postcard home describing their holiday and including certain essential facts about the planet.
- Students create a holiday poster for their chosen planet.
- To ensure students study all the planets the teacher could photocopy the best fact files and students could work on different ways of presenting this information:

  As a computerised database.

  As a spreadsheet.

  As a paper database.

  As a classroom display.

Planet Fact File

Comparing Earth with another planet

Name of our planet	Earth	Your choice of planet	
Distance across (Diameter)	km	Distance across (Diameter)	km
Temperature		Temperature	
Distance from sun		Distance from sun	
Number of moons		Number of moons	
Gravity		Gravity	
Time for one orbit of the sun (the planet's year)		Time for one orbit of the sun (the planet's year)	
Time for one spin (the planet's day)		Time for one spin (the planet's day)	

The atmosphere is made up of

The atmosphere is made up of

Special features about the planet:
Volcanoes? Craters? Storms? Rings? Moons?

Special features about the planet:
Volcanoes? Craters? Storms? Rings? Moons?

Your holiday on _____

What to pack

The temperature on this planet is _____°C

so it is _____ than Earth

You should pack

_____

_____

_____

The gravity is different to planet Earth which means

that _____

_____

So you should pack _____

_____

_____

Reaching the Planet

To reach this planet will take a long time. You will travel by _____

_____

Remember that the length of days and years is different to planet Earth

A year on this planet lasts for _____

A day on this planet is _____ hours long.

Because of this you can _____

_____

Things to do on _____

You will stay at _____

These are just some of the exciting events we have lined up for you during your holiday

1 _____

_____

2 _____

_____

3 _____

_____

_____ *is the perfect holiday destination*

You will have a brilliant time because

value for money

once in a lifetime

relax

unforgettable

enjoy

exciting

spectacular

Earthquakes - Preparation Notes

Subject: **Geography**

Topic: **Earthquakes**
Students work in pairs to find out about earthquakes and use their knowledge to create and play a board game.

Group: **Y8, S2**

Emphasis: **Curriculum**
Develop geographical understanding of earthquakes.
Design and realisation.

Information Skills
Locating information.
Reading for information.
Note taking.
Organising and presenting information creatively.

Personal Development
Creative use of information.
Seeing a project through from initial idea to practical conclusion.

Outcome: Board Game

Resources Provided

Steps to Learning, p4
A series of questions designed to help students plan their research and navigate their way through a project or task. The steps provide a consistent framework for all the projects in this book. In this case they are covered in the project planner.

Project Planner, p84-85
Written in a question and answer format to help students understand and plan their work.

Earthquake Survivor, p86-87
Passages to practise reading and note taking skills. The second passage has been adapted to be easier to read and to contain all the essential information but with less additional detail.

Designing the Game, p88-95
For ways to use these sheets, see Organisation and Planning, p81

Resources Required

The Library/LRC

A variety of books on earthquakes and natural disasters

The Guinness Book of Records or other books of amazing facts

Encyclopedias - text and electronic

The Internet

Search and Discover © Carel Press, Carlisle

Earthquakes - Organisation and Planning

Pre Lesson:

- Divide class into pairs.
- Obtain and organise resources. The National Earthquake Information Centre has a useful web site at: www.neic.cr.usgs.gov

Lesson 1 Introduction

In Library/LRC or classroom.

- Focus on **Steps to Learning** in the project planner.
- Explain spider diagrams. Give time for everyone to practise them, using the *Earthquake Survivor* passage and the outline on the project planner. Note that students will not find very much to say about *Before* and may have to make their own decision about what counts as *During* or *After*. Allow students to pool ideas about which points were important for their study of earthquakes.
- Students start their research. Emphasise that they will need to know what happens *Before*, *During* and *After* an earthquake.

Suggestions for working with the less able

Working as a class during the introductory stage may help students to identify with the structure of the project, and help them to see how it can be broken down into more manageable chunks.

As soon as the class reach the point where they are starting their research, you could allow a set time to research a question and then draw them together to discuss their answers. The continuity of bringing together and reviewing will help students remain on task. Further support for the less able is provided by the resource sheets.

Lesson 2 onwards

In Library/LRC continue research and design board game.

The principle of the game is to move around the board as quickly as possible. Challenges include:-

- Hot Spots – if a player lands on one of these they must answer a question about earthquakes.
- Keywords – if a player lands on one of these they must explain the meaning of a keyword.
- Instructions – e.g. You ignore the earthquake warning. Miss a turn.

Higher ability students may be able to design their own Hot Spot questions, Keywords and Instructions. Suggest to students that their board game must have 6 hot spots, 6 key words and several instruction squares.

Design Your Own Game, page 88, will help the **majority of students** to formulate their ideas.

For your **less able students,** or if you are simply short of time, you can use the structure provided by *Use the Game Board*, page 89:

- Game Board – pages 94-95 provide a game board based on the idea of circles radiating out from an epicentre. They can be joined together to make an A3 board but they would be even better if enlarged and then joined to make an A2 board.
- Hot Spot Questions – 12 prepared questions and a blank sheet for additional questions provided by you or by the students.
- Keywords – A list is included on *Use the Game Board*.

Rules – makes sure that students have established clear rules before they start to play.

What Next?

- Play the game – arguably the most enjoyable part of any design and realisation project is seeing the finished product in action!
- Swap games around class.
- Test out games with other classes, perhaps as a lunch time library activity.

Development

Work in partnership with another department such as art or design technology to extend the depth of the project. These departments could work on the design of the board game, while the library/geography side concentrates on the research.

USING THE EARTHQUAKES PROJECT PLANNER

The project planner is divided into Steps to Learning, each beginning with a question, the answer to which assists in the research process.

Explain that the project planner will help students understand the tasks and plan their work.

As a warm up exercise you could hold a class brainstorm to discuss what students already know about this topic.

Organise the class to work in pairs.

Opportunity to discuss available resources and for students to note down the different types.

It helps if students know early on how the finished product will look. If possible, show examples of board games already produced by other classes, or simple commercial board games.

Explain that most research begins with a question. Questions will help students focus on what needs to be looked up.

Project Planner - Earthquakes

What do I need to find out?

You are going to find out about **Earthquakes**

Who will I work with?
You will work with a partner to carry out your research.

Which resources will I use?
Fill in the blanks with the types of resource you will use during your research:

How will I present my work?
You will begin by making notes. Later on you will use your notes to design and make your own board game about earthquakes.

How should I start?
A good way to begin your research is to ask questions and look for the answers. Start by reading through the questions below. Discuss with your partner who is going to work on each question. Write that person's initials next to the question.

The Questions	Initials
Earthquakes Facts and Figures:	
What is an earthquake?	
Why do earthquakes happen?	
How do you measure earthquakes?	
Where are earthquakes likely to strike?	
During an earthquake:	
What happens during an earthquake?	
What should you do if you are caught in an earthquake?	
After an Earthquake:	
How are people rescued?	
How can survivors be helped?	
What can be done to stop future earthquakes damaging buildings?	

Search and Discover © Carel Press, Carlisle

Allow a few minutes for partners to read through the questions and decide who will work on each one. Although teamwork is important, students should try to work independently during the research stage. Emphasise the importance of the research stage – finding the information and making good notes is essential if the board game is to be successful.

Search and Discover © Carel Press, Carlisle

USING THE EARTHQUAKES PROJECT PLANNER

Ask everyone to jot down what they think is the purpose of taking notes. Compare views. Teacher-led discussion on note taking may be helpful. You could emphasise the importance of reading and understanding before writing anything down. Discuss why copying out is pointless, see the ideas given in the Introduction (p7)

Project Planner - Earthquakes

Making notes

One of the aims of this piece of work is to practise making notes. There are several different ways to make notes and you are going to use spider diagrams.

Before you start, let's have a practice run. You will be given the story of someone who survived an earthquake. Read the information, highlight the main points and then make notes on this spider diagram.

Notice that in this diagram we have started to organise the information for you.

Before

Earthquakes -
what happens

During

After

Allow about ten minutes for this exercise. Class feedback and discussion on the notes which have been made.

Check everyone is happy taking notes on spider diagrams.

Ensure students understand what a spider diagram is.

Your teacher will explain to you why making notes is important. Remember, your research is very important as you will use the information you find to design your board game.

Have I got all the information I need?

Check with your partner that all the questions have been answered. You should have a collection of spider diagrams with all your rough notes written on them.

Now you are ready to turn your rough notes into your board game!

Ask your teacher or librarian for your instructions.

Enjoy making the game!

Ask your teacher or librarian for a SELF-EVALUATION sheet and record how well you think you have done.

Search and Discover © Carel Press, Carlisle   85

Delay discussion of this until at least one full lesson has been spent on the research stage. Higher ability students should be able to cope with making their own rules independently. For lower ability students it may be advisable to go through the instructions as a class or group when everyone has completed the research stage.

Encourage students to self evaluate.

Project Planner - Earthquakes

What do I need to find out?

You are going to find out about **Earthquakes**

Who will I work with?
You will work with a partner to carry out your research.

Which resources will I use?
Fill in the blanks with the types of resource you will use during your research:

How will I present my work?
You will begin by making notes. Later on you will use your notes to design and make your own board game about earthquakes.

How should I start?
A good way to begin your research is to ask questions and look for the answers. Start by reading through the questions below. Discuss with your partner who is going to work on each question. Write that person's initials next to the question.

The Questions	Initials
Earthquake Facts and Figures:	
What is an earthquake?	
Why do earthquakes happen?	
How do you measure earthquakes?	
Where are earthquakes likely to strike?	
During an earthquake:	
What happens during an earthquake?	
What should you do if you are caught in an earthquake?	
After an Earthquake:	
How are people rescued?	
How can survivors be helped?	
What can be done to stop future earthquakes damaging buildings?	

Project Planner - Earthquakes

Making notes

One of the aims of this piece of work is to practise making notes. There are several different ways to make notes and you are going to use spider diagrams.

Before you start, let's have a practice run. You will be given the story of someone who survived an earthquake. Read the information, highlight the main points and then make notes on this spider diagram.

Notice that in this diagram we have started to organise the information for you.

Your teacher will explain to you why making notes is important. Remember, your research is very important as you will use the information you find to design your board game.

Have I got all the information I need?

Check with your partner that all the questions have been answered. You should have a collection of spider diagrams with all your rough notes written on them.

Now you are ready to turn your rough notes into your board game!

Ask your teacher or librarian for your instructions.

Enjoy making the game!

Ask your teacher or librarian for a SELF-EVALUATION sheet and record how well you think you have done.

Earthquake Survivor

In August 1999 I was on holiday with my Mum and Dad in Turkey. We had an apartment in a small town.

It must have been about two or three o'clock in the morning when I opened my eyes because I thought that someone was shaking me. The whole room was rocking like a boat in a storm. At first I couldn't understand what was happening but then I realised that we were in the middle of an earthquake!

The next thing I knew I was lying on the floor with our cases on top of me – they had been thrown across the room! I tried to stand up but I kept falling down.

I shouted for my Mum and Dad who were in the next room. Suddenly, a huge crack appeared in the dividing wall. I managed to crawl under the table and hide as the wall between the rooms just crumbled away.

At least I could see Mum and Dad now. They were covered in dust and Mum was holding her arm and crying. Dad had a big gash on his head. I started to panic and screamed, "Dad, Dad, help me!" He told me to crawl to him and that we had to get out of the building.

The rooms were still shaking but we crawled to the door and found the stairs. It was pitch dark and we could only move very slowly. The tremors were coming every few minutes. The stairs were covered with bits of rubble and glass. We had to be very careful where we stepped but the building was shaking so much that we did not know where to put our feet.

Outside it was even more frightening. Everyone was crying and screaming. People were running madly around or desperately digging at the rubble, wailing. Many of them were covered in blood. We could see hands and legs sticking out from the rubble but it was impossible to say whether these people were alive or dead.

I could hear sirens in the distance but the roads were full of bricks and concrete. Shops and cafes were just ruins. All around us buildings were still crashing down as the earth shook.

Mum said we should go to the park near to the hotel to get away from the falling buildings.

In the distance we could see fires coming from the demolished buildings. The air tasted of dust and smoke. It looked like the end of the world.

Every now and then the earth would tremble again. We sat in that park, numb with shock, all the rest of the night and most of the next day. As the day became hotter we began to realise that we had had no food and water and we would not be getting any! As the day wore on people came into the park from further down the hill and we heard that the coast had been hit by a tidal wave. This had brought salt water and mud inland and had polluted all the freshwater supplies.

Towards the end of the day, soldiers began to arrive to rescue survivors and to help with the digging. We were taken in an army lorry heading for Istanbul.

The journey was very slow. The roads were jammed with cars and people trying to get away from the centre of the earthquake. Everyone was afraid that there would be more big tremors and there were still rumblings and aftershocks happening. The road was split and crumbling in places.

Eventually we reached the British Embassy. We were starving and desperately thirsty. We had no belongings, but at least we could go home to our own house and a country not at risk of terrible earthquakes.

We were so lucky not to die. I can't forget as well that there are people who lost their homes, possessions, families and lives in a few hours.

Earthquake Survivor

In August 1999, I was on holiday with my Mum and Dad in Turkey. One night, I woke up because I thought someone was shaking me. The whole room was rocking like a boat in a storm. I suddenly realised it was an earthquake. A huge crack appeared in the bedroom wall. I crawled out of bed and hid under a table. I watched as the wall just crumbled away. Now I could see my Mum and Dad in the next room. They were covered in dust. Dad had a big gash on his head.

Together we crawled downstairs. The tremors were coming every few minutes and the stairs were shaking. Outside, everyone was crying and screaming. Everywhere we looked, buildings had fallen down. We could see arms and legs sticking out from the rubble.

I could hear sirens in the distance. We could see fires coming from the demolished buildings. It was like the end of the world.

We went to a park with lots of other survivors. Hours went by. It was very hot and we had no food or water. We heard that the earthquake had caused a tidal wave. Finally soldiers arrived. Some of them began to dig through the rubble to rescue people.

We were taken in a lorry to Istanbul. We could feel aftershocks and everyone was scared in case there were more big tremors. Finally we got on an aeroplane to go home. We were so lucky to survive.

Design Your Own Game

If you are designing your own game:

Decide what shape the game should take. Your teacher has an example which might give you ideas. Try to keep it simple!

Think about the aim of the game, which should be to get around the board as quickly as possible.

Think about the challenges around the board. Here are some suggestions that you could place on some of the squares:

6 Hot Spots

When you land on these you have to answer a question about earthquakes. You could make up the questions based on your own research, some could be difficult and some easy. You will need more than six questions because different people may land on the same Hot Spot.

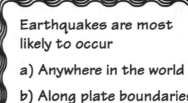

Earthquakes are most likely to occur

a) Anywhere in the world

b) Along plate boundaries

c) In Tokyo

d) In the earth's core.

6 Keywords

On some squares you could write down keywords about earthquakes. If someone lands on one of these they have to explain what the keyword means.

Richter Scale

6 Instructions

On some squares you may give players an instruction connected with earthquakes.

You must decide what the rewards and punishments will be – the possibilities are endless.

You forgot to stand in a doorway when the earthquake struck. Miss a turn.

Use the Game Board

If you are using the board included in this pack:

Give your game a name and write it in the boxes on the board.

Decide on starting and finishing points and write them on the board. Number the squares.

The arrows let you move from one circle to another.

Hot Spots

When you land on these you have to answer a question about earthquakes. You could make up the questions based on your own research. Some questions could be difficult and some easy. Or you can use the questions that are already prepared and add some of your own.

Earthquakes are most likely to occur

a) Anywhere in the world

b) Along plate boundaries

c) In Tokyo

d) In the earth's core.

Keywords

On these squares you could write down keywords about earthquakes. If someone lands on that square they have to explain what the keyword means. Some possible keywords are:

Fault Line
Epicentre
Tsunami
San Andreas Fault
Core
Crust
Mantle
Earthquake Zone
Magnitude
Richter Scale
Focus

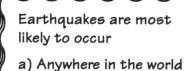

Richter Scale

Instructions

On these squares you may give players an instruction connected with earthquakes.

You must decide what the rewards and punishments will be.

You forgot to stand in a doorway when the earthquake struck. Miss a turn.

Rules

Now write your rules:

1   This game is for _____ players

2   The aim of the game is to _____

_____

3   You win by _____

_____

4   You will need (tick only the ones you will use)

counters	☐	dice	☐
Hot Spot cards	☐	Instruction Squares	☐
timer	☐	Keyword Squares	☐
paper	☐	pencils	☐

5   To start you have to _____

6   What happens when you answer a Hot Spot question?

If you get it right you _____

_____

If you get it wrong you_____

_____

7   What happens when you land on other special squares e.g. the ones

with arrows or the ones with instructions?_____

_____

_____

8   Are there any other special features of your game e.g. time limits,
things players have to do?

_____

_____

Search and Discover © Carel Press, Carlisle

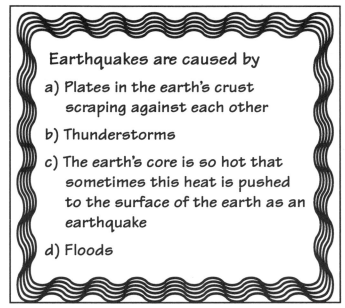

Earthquakes are caused by

a) Plates in the earth's crust scraping against each other

b) Thunderstorms

c) The earth's core is so hot that sometimes this heat is pushed to the surface of the earth as an earthquake

d) Floods

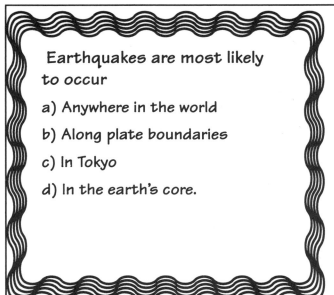

Earthquakes are most likely to occur

a) Anywhere in the world

b) Along plate boundaries

c) In Tokyo

d) In the earth's core.

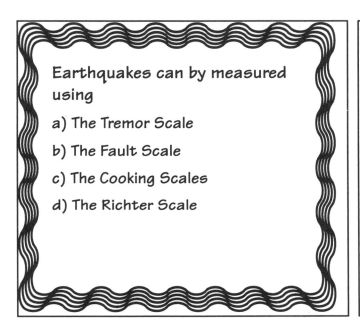

Earthquakes can by measured using

a) The Tremor Scale

b) The Fault Scale

c) The Cooking Scales

d) The Richter Scale

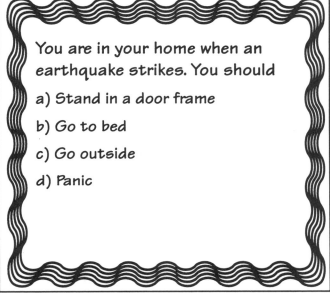

You are in your home when an earthquake strikes. You should

a) Stand in a door frame

b) Go to bed

c) Go outside

d) Panic

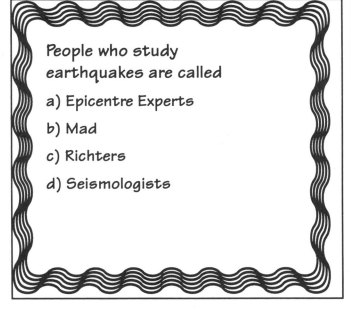

People who study earthquakes are called

a) Epicentre Experts

b) Mad

c) Richters

d) Seismologists

List three things you may see during an earthquake

Straight after an earthquake you should

a) Make a drink

b) Phone for help

c) Stay where you are in case of aftershocks

d) Start moving rubble

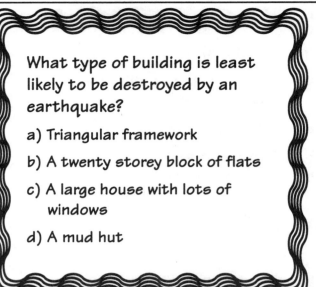

What type of building is least likely to be destroyed by an earthquake?

a) Triangular framework

b) A twenty storey block of flats

c) A large house with lots of windows

d) A mud hut

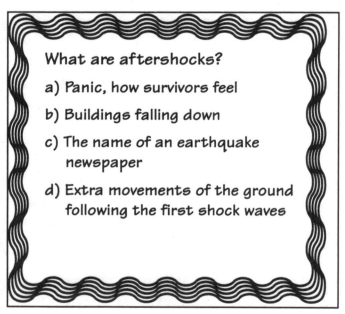

What are aftershocks?

a) Panic, how survivors feel

b) Buildings falling down

c) The name of an earthquake newspaper

d) Extra movements of the ground following the first shock waves

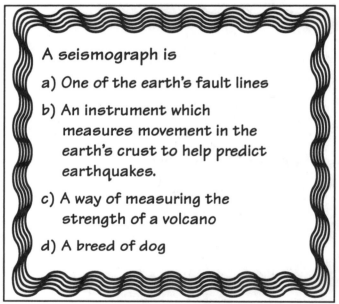

A seismograph is

a) One of the earth's fault lines

b) An instrument which measures movement in the earth's crust to help predict earthquakes.

c) A way of measuring the strength of a volcano

d) A breed of dog

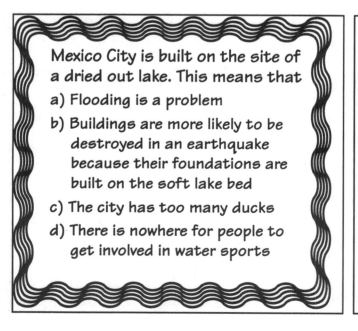

Mexico City is built on the site of a dried out lake. This means that

a) Flooding is a problem

b) Buildings are more likely to be destroyed in an earthquake because their foundations are built on the soft lake bed

c) The city has too many ducks

d) There is nowhere for people to get involved in water sports

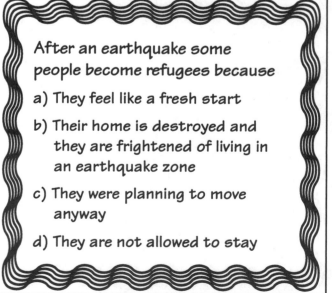

After an earthquake some people become refugees because

a) They feel like a fresh start

b) Their home is destroyed and they are frightened of living in an earthquake zone

c) They were planning to move anyway

d) They are not allowed to stay

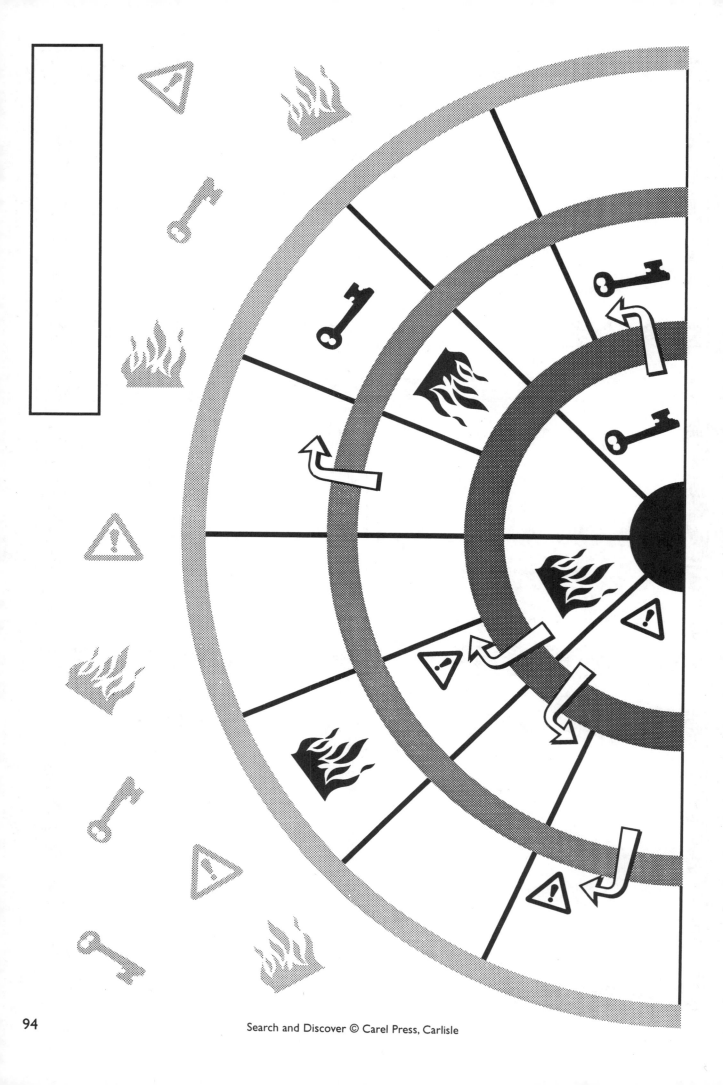

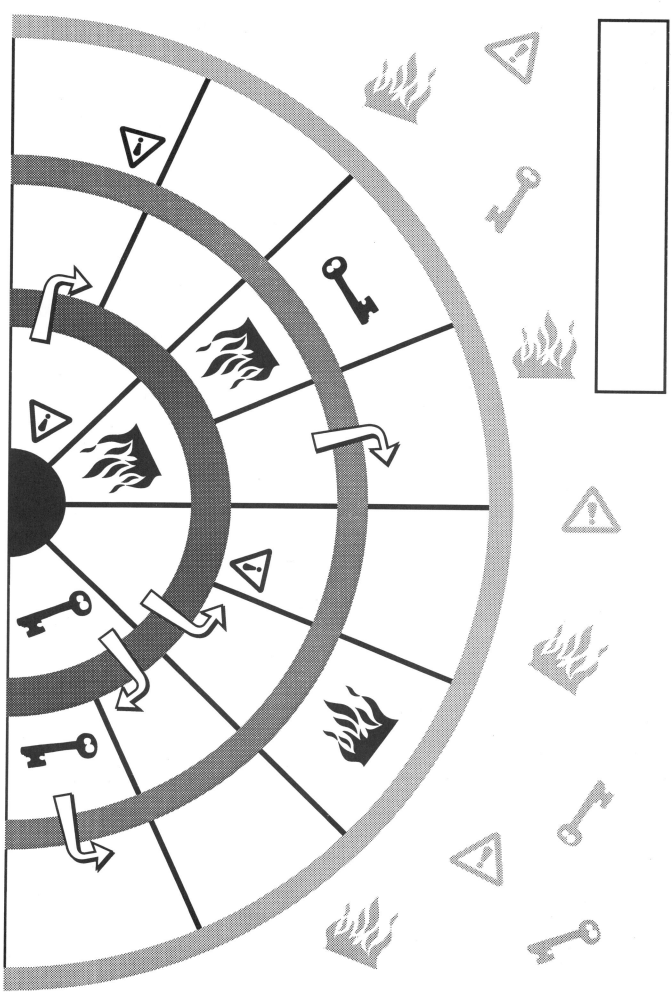

DEBATE – PREPARATION NOTES

Subject: **English**

Topic: **Speaking and Listening**
Students work in a group of four to research arguments for and against a specific statement. They then divide into pairs to write and deliver a speech.

Group: **Y9, S3**

OUTCOME:
DEBATE

Aims: **Curriculum**
Develop a logical argument.
Write and speak persuasively.
Listen to and appreciate other points of view.

Information Skills
Locating information.
Reading for information.
Note taking.
Analysing and interpreting information.
Presenting information persuasively.

Personal Development
Understand the value and organisation of a debate.

Resources Provided

Steps to Learning, p4
The steps to learning are a series of questions designed to help students plan their research and navigate their way through a project or task. The steps provide a consistent framework for all the projects in this book.

Statements for Debate, p98
This list of statements is meant as a starting point and is not prescriptive. It is based on experience of availability of resources.

Notes Grid, p99
Assists students during the early stage of their research in finding arguments for and against their chosen statement. Designed to discourage copying and to encourage students to use a variety of information sources.

Arguments and Evidence Sheet, p100
Helps students to specify evidence to back up and develop their line of argument. Students may need more than one sheet.

Preparing the Debate, p101
Offers suggestions and help in writing and speaking persuasively.

Resources Required

The Library/LRC

A wide variety of books on the subjects being debated

Encyclopedias (text and electronic)

Essential Articles (Carel Press)

Fact File (Carel Press)

Key Organisations (Carel Press)

Information from charities and pressure groups.

Debate – Organisation and Planning

Pre Lesson

- Divide class into groups of four.
- Decide which statements students will research. This may depend on available resources and the focus of your current work. Ten suggestions are given on p98 but these are by no means exhaustive!
- Obtain and organise resources.
- Obtain a video or a recorded example of debate.

Lesson 1 Introduction

Focus on steps to learning

1 What do I need to find out?

Brief explanation of this project and how it fits in to past and future learning.

2 What do I already know?

Students familiarise themselves with the statements, and brainstorm within their groups. Encourage them to realise that they may already know something about many of the topics for debate. At this point students need to know which statement they will be working on. This may be decided by you or by them.

3 Who will I work with?

Opportunity to set out parameters and emphasise team work. Students could work in a group of four initially and then divide into pairs to work on the arguments for and against.

4 Which resources will I use?

Discuss available resources. You may also wish to introduce general sources of current material, such as *Essential Articles* which contains issue pieces on a wide range of subjects and *Fact File* which has current statistics. You may also wish to use ephemeral material, such as brochures and pamphlets, which may be available from charities and pressure groups. *Key Organisations* is an annually updated list of such organisations.

5 How should I present my work?

Opportunity to discuss the role and importance of debates. If possible show an example of a debate (perhaps from TV) or you could even film some of the debates by other classes.

6 How should I start?

Emphasise the importance of finding arguments for and against and then backing these up with evidence. The *Notes Grid* and *Arguments and Evidence Sheet* can be demonstrated here.

Lesson 2 onwards

In Library/LRC continuing research and preparing for debate.

7 Have I got the information I need?

Ensure sufficient arguments and evidence have been collected. Students may be tempted to rush the research stage – you could emphasise that the success of their debate depends almost entirely on the quality of evidence they can put forward. If several arguments have been collected students may wish to pick three of the most persuasive.

8 What should I do with the information?

Students now need to use *Preparing the Debate* to assist them in writing their presentation. Teacher input may be needed here as writing and presenting a debate is likely to be a completely new experience. Filming some of the debates can be helpful in providing feedback and for demonstrating to future classes. If several classes are doing the same project, a grand final could involve all of them, perhaps (if you're feeling brave) during assembly.

9 What have I achieved?

The debate itself is a visible indication of student achievement. Spending time watching and constructively criticising some of the filmed debates will also be helpful. Prizes could be awarded for best speaker, most persuasive arguments, greatest effort etc.

What Next?

- This could be the basis for further work on topics for debate or for argumentative writing.
- Switch roles and argue the completely opposite case.

Statements for Debate

Young people should put up with bullying and accept it as part of growing up.

Ghosts really exist.

Capital punishment is the right sentence for certain crimes. Bring back capital punishment.

Fox hunting is a cruel and unnecessary sport and should be banned.

There are no circumstances in which it would be acceptable to perform any kind of scientific or medical experiments on animals.

Too much violence on television and at the cinema can influence the way young people behave. The only solution is to stop young people from watching anything violent.

Excluding badly behaved students does not solve the problem of bad behaviour. Schools should not be allowed to do this.

Everything we need to know we can find out on the internet. Books are no longer necessary because the internet has all the answers.

Boxing is a dangerous sport and should be banned.

Genetically modified food is perfectly safe; everyone is making a big fuss about nothing.

Debate – Notes Grid

Names of people in the group ....

....

Name of topic _____

Debate title _____

_____

Source	An argument in favour	Source	An argument against

When you have researched arguments in favour of and against the statement, decide in your group, which pair are going to argue in favour of the motion and which are going to argue against.

Next you need to do further research to find evidence to back up your arguments. Evidence may be in the form of statistics, the opinion of an expert or specialist organisation or a real life story.

DEBATE - ARGUMENT & EVIDENCE

Names ....

Debate title: _____

_____

Are you arguing FOR or AGAINST? _____

Argument:

Evidence

Real life story ☐   statistics ☐   opinion of person/organisation ☐

Argument:

Evidence

Real life story ☐   statistics ☐   opinion of person/organisation ☐

PREPARING THE DEBATE

You have researched the arguments for and against the statement. You've found some evidence to back them up. It's now time to write your speech for the debate.

Remember

The aim is to persuade people to vote for your point of view.

- Be logical – present your arguments and evidence carefully.

- Aim to present three strong arguments with plenty of evidence – If you offer too many arguments people will get confused, bored and stop listening.

- Be persuasive – make people sympathetic and get them on your side.

You can do this in several ways:

Statistics

These can help to shock people and make what you have to say sound more dramatic.

> Last year 24,000 people died through smoking related diseases

Real life stories

These make what you have to say seem more believable. People are more likely to listen and remember because they get involved in the story.

> I'm going to tell you a story. James was an ordinary 15 year old boy who was bullied.
> This is what happened to him...

Build up what you have to say

> This year 24,000 people have died through smoking related diseases.

> Here is some information which will shock you. One day it could even happen to you. This year 24,000 people have died through smoking related diseases.

Which statement sounds most dramatic?

Use strong and dramatic language

Think of the power of words like:

suffering, anguish, disaster, fear, hate, pain, trauma, misery, terror

Preparation Notes

Subject: **RE, Citizenship, English**

Topic: **Charities**:
Students work in groups to research themes such as homelessness, the environment, teenage problems. Next they research a charity or charities working on this issue.

Group: **Y9/S3**

Emphasis: **Curriculum**
Understand social issues
Understand work of local, national and international voluntary agencies

Information Skills
Formulating research questions
Locating information
Reading and note-taking
Analysing and interpreting information
Presenting information in a variety of formats

Personal Development
Communication skills
Empathy with and appreciation of different situations.

Outcome

Radio or TV appeal

Radio or TV Interview

Response to Letters

Resources Provided

Steps to Learning, p4
The **Steps to Learning** are a series of questions designed to help students plan their research and navigate their way through a project or task. The steps provide a consistent framework for all the projects in this book.

Addresses, p104
These are provided to help the teacher/librarian prepare for the project. For a wide range of addresses, annually updated, see *Key Organisations* from Carel Press.

Brainstorming, p105 & Questions to Ask, p106
A range of themes could be tackled. *Brainstorming* enables higher ability students to focus on suitable questions. *Questions to ask* offers suggestions for those who need help to get started.

Research, p107
Helps students to organise their research on the charity which relates to their theme.

Appeal, p108, Scripts, p109-110, Interview, p111 & Letters to the Editor, p112-116
Students choose one or more of the above outcomes as a way of presenting their research.

Resources Required

The Library/LRC

Books and information on social themes.

Encyclopedias (text and electronic)

Information from charities and pressure groups.

Organisation and Planning

Pre Lesson

- Divide class into pairs.
- Decide which themes are to be researched. There are some suggestions on page 104, but many more current addresses of charities and campaigning organisations are available in *Key Organisations* from Carel Press.
- Obtain and organise resources, including information from the charities which are to be researched.

  It is best if the librarian or teacher requests the information from the charities in advance, to be prepared for this project and to avoid multiple requests. Most charities, especially smaller ones, appreciate a stamped, addressed envelope.

  It may be advisable to direct your less able students towards issues which are likely to be within their experience.

- Have access to tape recorders and /or video camera to record appeals and interviews.

Lesson 1 Introduction
In Library/ LRC or classroom

Focus on steps to learning:

1 What do I need to find out?

Brief explanation of this project and how it fits in to past and future learning.

2 What do I already know?

Introduce students to the social themes. Choose one of them and hold a class discussion. Most students will have some knowledge and opinions about a theme such as homelessness or children's rights. This will help to focus their thoughts and build their confidence.

3 Who will I work with?

Opportunity to set out parameters and emphasise team work.

4 Which resources will I use?

Discuss available resources. Emphasise resources which may be unfamiliar such as information received from charities.

5 How should I present my work?

Explain that everyone can use their research for a range of different outcomes including creating a charity appeal, conducting interviews or responding to the letters on pages 112-116. Show students examples of possible outcomes, either from other classes, or, if this is the first time you have done the topic, you could make up a couple yourself.

6 How should I start?

Students are either allocated or choose a social theme. They begin by formulating research questions about their theme using the keywords **how, why, what** etc to help them. Students may be inexperienced at formulating their own questions, so teacher input will be invaluable. For the least able you may want to use the questions on page 105. Once the questions have been decided on, students need to research the answers. Spider diagrams could be used for note-taking.

Lesson 2 onwards
In Library/LRC continuing research and preparing appeal

7 Have I got the information I need?

Ensure sufficient research has been carried out. Students may be tempted to rush this stage, so emphasise that the success of their TV/Radio appeal or interview depends largely on the quality of their research.

8 What should I do with the information?

Once the research is finished the outcome needs to be decided. This may be directed by you, or you may prefer to give students a free choice. Some students may do more than one - for example creating the charity appeal and writing a letter. Explain that whatever is chosen, a mixture of fact and imagination will be needed. The Radio/TV appeal frameworks and Interview sheets will be essential to help students plan their work. Remind them to use the research they have already carried out to help them fulfil their chosen outcome.

9 What have I achieved?

Encourage students to evaluate their own work. What have they enjoyed doing? What did they find difficult or easy? What do they feel they have learned?

What Next?

- Spend a lesson watching students perform the charity appeals, another lesson could be spent watching the interviews. Discuss what makes a successful appeal.
- Create a display of responses to the letters. Discuss the importance of writing persuasively.
- Students survey their local area to find out about voluntary organisations and possibly interview or survey charity workers to further their research.

Elderly People

Help the Aged
16-18 St James' Walk
London
EC1R OBE
Tel: 020 7253 0253
Fax: 020 7250 4474
hta@dial.pipex.com
www.helptheaged.org.uk

Teenagers

Childline
Freepost 1111
London N1 0BR
Royal Mail Building
Studd Street
London N1 OQW
Helpline: 0800 1111
Tel: 020 7239 1000 (Admin)
Fax: 020 7239 1001
http://www.childline.org.uk

Childline Scotland
18 Albion St
Glasgow G1 1LH
Helpline: 0800 1111
Tel: 0141 552 1123
Fax: 0141 552 3089
www.childline.org.uk

Children's Rights

NSPCC (Nat. Soc. for the Prevention of Cruelty to Children)
42 Curtain Rd
London EC2A 3NH
Tel: 020 7825 2500
Fax: 020 7825 2525
info@nspcc.org.uk
www.nspcc.org.uk

Children 1st
(Royal Scottish Soc. for Prevention of Cruelty to Children)
41 Polwarth Terrace
Edinburgh EH11 1NU
Helpline: 0808 800 2222
Tel: 0131 337 8539
Fax: 0131 346 8284
children1st@zetnet.co.uk

Free the Children – International
freechild@clo.com
www.freethechildren.org

Poverty

Barnardo's
Tanners Lane
Barkingside
Ilford IG6 1QG
Tel: 020 8550 8822
Fax: 020 8551 6870
pdubarnardos@compuserve.com
www.barnardos.org.uk

Child Poverty Action Group
94 White Lion St
London N1 9PF
Tel: 020 7837 7979
Fax: 020 7837 6414
staff@cpag.demon.co.uk

Developing World

Comic Relief
5th Floor
89 Albert Embankment
London SE1 7TP
Tel: 020 7820 5555
Fax: 020 7820 5500
red@comicrelief.org.uk
www.comicrelief.org.uk

Oxfam
274 Banbury Rd
Oxford OX2 7DZ
Tel: 01865 311311
Fax: 01865 312600
oxfam@oxfam.org.uk
www.oxfam.org.uk

Action Aid
Chataway House
Leach Rd
Chard
Somerset TA20 1FR
Tel: 01460 238000
Fax: 01460 67191
mail@actionaid.org.uk
www.oneworld.org/actionaid

Animal Rights

RSPCA (Royal Soc. for the Prevention of Cruelty to Animals)
Causeway
Horsham
West Sussex RH12 1HG
Tel: 01403 264181
Fax: 01403 241048
enqserv@rspca.org.uk
www.rspca.org.uk

The Environment

Friends of the Earth
26-28 Underwood St
London N1 7JQ
Tel: 020 7490 1555
Fax: 020 7490 0881
info@foe.co.uk
www.foe.co.uk/
&
72 Newhaven Rd
Edinburgh EH6 5QG
Tel: 0131 554 9977
Fax: 0131 554 8656
foescotland@gn.apc.org
www.foe-scotland.org.uk

Disabled People's Rights

Disability Alliance
Universal House
88-94 Wentworth St
London E1 7SA
Tel: 020 7247 8776
Tel: 020 7247 8763 Rights Advice Line
(Mon & Wed 2pm-4pm)
Fax: 020 7247 8765

Scope (formerly the Spastics Soc.)
PO Box 833
Milton Keynes MK14 6HW
Helpline: 0800 626 216 (9am-9pm weekdays, 2pm-6pm Sat & Sun)
Fax: 020 7619 7399
cphelpline@scope.org.uk
www.scope.org.uk

The Homeless

Shelter
88 Old St
London EC1V 9HU
Shelterline: 0808 800 4444
Tel: 020 7505 2000
Fax: 020 7505 2169
shelter_supporters@compuserve.com
www.shelter.org.uk

Shelter (Cymru)
25 Walter Road
Swansea SA1 5NN
Helpline: 0808 800 4444
Tel: 01792 469400
Fax: 01792 460050

Shelter (Scotland)
4th Floor, Scotiabank House
6 South Charlotte Street
Edinburgh EH2 4AW
Helpline: 0808 800 4444
Tel: 0131 473 7170
Fax: 0131 473 7199
shelter_scotland@compuserve.com
www.shelter.org.uk

Brainstorming

The theme I am going to research is:

These are the keywords I am going to use to help me:

How?   What?   Why?   Who?   When?   Where?

These are the questions I could ask about my theme:

1 _____

_____

2 _____

_____

3 _____

_____

4 _____

_____

Check your questions with your teacher or librarian

These are some of the resources that will help me answer the questions:

Author   Title

Questions to ask

Poverty

What does poverty mean? Who in Britain is poor?

Why does poverty mean different things in different countries?

What is it like to be poor? How can the poor be helped?

The Homeless

Why do people become homeless?

Who might become homeless?

Where do homeless people go?

What can be done to help the homeless?

Developing World

Where is the Developing World?

What are some of the problems that people living in developing countries face?

How can these problems be addressed?

The Elderly

Why are there more elderly people today?

What problems do elderly people face?

How can elderly people be helped?

Animal Rights

What are animal rights?

Why does animal cruelty happen?

What can be done to solve the problem?

Teenagers

What is it like to be a teenager today?

What sort of problems do teenagers face?

Who can teenagers go to for help with their problems?

How can these problems be solved?

The Environment

What is happening to our environment?

Why do we need to protect it?

What will happen if we do nothing?

What can be done to improve the environment?

Children's Rights

What rights do children have?

Why do children's rights mean different things in different countries?

What can be done to promote chidren's rights?

Can children themselves do anything to protect their rights?

Disabled People

What are disabilities?

Who might be faced with a disability?

What problems do disabled people face?

What can be done to help disabled people?

Name of Charity

Year established

Why it was set up

Charity's main aim (Try to sum this up in one or two sentences)

What kind of people and situations does this charity aim to help?

How does the charity raise money?

Are there any special projects the charity has set up or been involved in?

Appeal

Now you have done some research on your charity you are going to design a radio or TV appeal to persuade people to donate money to the charity.

Here's how to do it.

You need to grab people's attention so the appeal should start with a story telling listeners/viewers about someone who is in great need of help.

Make up the following information about a person who could be helped by the charity

Name of person: _____ Age: _____

Where the person lives: _____

Who the person lives with (if anybody) _____

_____

You are going to explain why this person needed the help of the charity so you need to describe the person's situation.

What could have happened to this person?   What problems does this person face?

How can the charity help this person?

Script - Person

Now you need to write your script. Use this writing framework to help you.

This is a special appeal for charity. Our charity today is
_____

First of all we would like to tell you about someone who was helped by the charity. His/her name is_____

Let me tell you something about this person.

_____was facing lots of problems. One of the problems was...

Another problem was...

This is what the charity did to help...

Now _____'s situation has improved because...

We need your help to raise money for this charity because...

This is what you can do to help...

Now you need to write your script. Use this writing framework to help you.

This is a special appeal for charity. Our charity today is
_____
First of all we would like to tell you about a situation which was improved by the charity. Let me tell you about the situation...

This situation caused lots of problems. One of the problems was....

Another problem was...

This is what the charity did to help...

Now the situation has improved because...

This story had a happy ending but we still need your help to raise money for this charity because...

This is what you can do to help...

Interview

You are going to conduct an interview for a TV programme with a charity worker and with someone who has been helped by the charity.

These are some of the questions you could ask the charity worker:

Why is this charity important to you?

What does this charity do?

Why did you want to work for the charity?

Tell us about some of the things the charity has done to help people.

What kind of jobs are available for someone who wanted to work for the charity?

Do you get paid for working for the charity?

How do you raise money for the charity?

You could add some questions of your own

These are some of the questions you could ask the person who has been helped by the charity:

Why did you need help from the charity?

How has the charity helped you?

What do you think would have happened to you if the charity had not been able to help you?

What would you say to people to encourage them to give money to charity?

You could add some questions of your own

Dear Editor,

I have just received a letter from **Oxfam** asking for donations to help some third world country I've never even heard of. The saying "Charity begins at home" is very true, so why should we help a load of people who live thousands of miles away? What's the point of giving them money to buy food when they'll only spend it on guns to hold wars against each other. The reason they haven't got enough to eat is because they're just too lazy to work and would rather rely on handouts from hard working people like me!

Yours sincerely,
R S Stevens, Barnford

Dear Editor,

What is the point of a charity like **Comic Relief**? They are just a bunch of stupid people who think that having fun is more important than raising money. I ask you – Red Nose Day, sitting in a bath of baked beans, holding a snail race. What's the point? Fund raising is a serious issue and all these ridiculous notions make it seem stupid. As for all the so called celebrities who get involved, they're only doing it for the publicity and all the money they must make out of it. It's about time people took charity fund raising a little more seriously.

Yours in anger,
P Evans (Mrs)

Dear Editor,

I have just received a letter from **Friends of the Earth** asking for donations.

In my opinion they are just a bunch of hippies who want to spend my hard earned cash saving some ancient tree or trying to protect a pointless breed of insect in the middle of the Amazon Rain Forest. Why don't they look closer to home and come and clean out my local canal which is full of rubbish and shopping trolleys? I'm sure half the stuff we read about global warming and endangered species isn't even true. It's just a way of frightening people into donating money so they can spend it on their harebrained schemes. Well they won't be getting any money from me!

Z Kowalski (Mr)

Dear Editor,

My Sunday morning listening was interrupted by a radio advertisement for **Barnardo's** asking for donations to help poor families. I cannot believe that people today are still going on about how poor they are. They've all got satellite TV and videos and just waste money on cigarettes and alcohol. There's so many government handouts today, how can anyone complain about being poor? These people should get off their backsides and do a day's work instead of lounging around moaning. Charities like Barnardo's just make the problem worse. I bet Barnardo's just gives out money left, right and centre to anyone who complains about being poor. Well they won't be getting a donation from me!

Philip Simons

Letters to the Editor

Dear Editor,

This morning's post brought another begging letter from **Help the Aged** asking for donations. Why on earth should I give them anything? What's so special about getting old; you don't hear of a charity called "Help the Middle Aged" or "Help the Twenty-Somethings"! Old people should sort themselves out. They don't have to go to work any more so they've got all day to get themselves up and have breakfast; they shouldn't need anyone to help them. As for being lonely, well their families should do more to keep them company. I've got four children who have promised to look after me when I get old. Charities for the elderly are just ridiculous - they make this huge problem out of something that's going to happen to all of us and what on earth can a charity do to make getting old any less horrible?

Mrs N Bussue

Dear Editor,

Today I received a letter from the **NSPCC** asking for donations. Well they won't be getting any money from me! Child cruelty indeed. When I was a child my parents beat me many times and it didn't do me any harm. As for emotional cruelty what's that supposed to mean? Kids today are just too sensitive. They should toughen up. A bit of ridicule and bullying never hurt anyone. Children today have it easy; the worst punishment they get at school is a detention and at home all that seems to happen is getting 'grounded'. No one hits children anymore, so I really can't see the point of a charity like the NSPCC.

A Concerned Pensioner, Accrington

Search and Discover © Carel Press, Carlisle

Dear Editor,

This morning I was stopped in the street by a collector for **Shelter** asking for donations to help the so-called homeless. I am sick and tired of seeing homeless people lying in doorways and begging for money. I'm sure if I gave them any it would only be spent on drink and drugs. Homeless people should get themselves a proper job and smarten up their act. No one needs to be homeless in this day and age and charities like Shelter just make things worse by giving these people handouts.

Yours,
P R Raj

Dear Editor,

I have just seen an advertisement from the **RSPCA** asking for donations. Why on earth should we help animals when people are so much more important? Every day hundreds of people are in desperate need of help and yet the RSPCA expects us to donate money to help animals. Animals are all very nice, but you can't tell me that an animal really experiences suffering. They're not as intelligent as us humans, so how can they have the same feelings? What does the RSPCA actually do anyway? Rescue a few cats and dogs and pay an awful lot of inspectors to walk around in silly uniforms?

Mr B Hart

Dear Editor,

I was disturbed to see a TV advertisement from **Scope** asking for donations. Well it's nothing to do with me. I'm sorry for people who are disabled, but really they would all be better off in hospitals where they could be looked after properly. I think a charity like Scope just raises their hopes by making them think they should stay with their families or even look after themselves. I mean, how can they? It's hard enough for able bodied people like me to cope in our busy society. The disabled should just accept that they're different and not try to live the way we do.

Name and Address Supplied

Dear Editor,

Recently you printed an advertisement from **Childline** asking for donations. You must be joking! I am disgusted by the behaviour of teenagers today. They all seem to hang around on street corners in huge groups terrifying innocent people like me. They are all cheeky and lazy. They moan about their problems and worry about ridiculous things like being bullied and falling out with their friends. Childline just makes the problem worse – fancy offering these teenagers a free phone number to ring every time they've got a problem. What sort of phone calls do they get ? I bet it's things like "My Mum won't let me stay up to watch South Park, what should I do?" A so-called charity like Childline is a complete waste of money, if teenagers have problems they should talk to their parents or sort it out themselves.

N Cassidy (Miss),
East Hetherington

SELF EVALUATION

Name _____   How I think I did!

The topic I have researched is: _____

This is how I felt about doing this project: ☺   😐   ☹
because _____

This is how I felt about working in the Library/LRC: ☺   😐   ☹
because _____

The resources which I found easiest to use were:

because...

The resources which I found hardest to use were:

because...

The thing I did not enjoy about this project was...

The thing I enjoyed most about this project was...

I would award my project   [/10]

If I was doing this piece of work again I might improve it by...

Notes Grid

	Research Question or Theme:	Research Question or Theme:	Research Question or Theme:
Source:			
Source:			
Source:			

Spider Diagram

ACTIVE LISTENING

Report by ....

When you are listening to a speech, try to think about the points the speakers are making, as well as the quality of their presentation.

This is a list of some of the things we should be looking for during a presentation or debate. Mark each box according to how well each person or group has achieved these objectives.

Yes	☑	Score 2 points
Sometimes	S	Score 1 point
No	✗	Score 0 points

GROUP	1	2	3	4	5	6
Did you hear everything that was said?	☐	☐	☐	☐	☐	☐
Did you understand the arguments put forward?	☐	☐	☐	☐	☐	☐
Did the speakers use their voices expressively?	☐	☐	☐	☐	☐	☐
Was the speech interesting?	☐	☐	☐	☐	☐	☐
Did the speaker(s) seem to enjoy themselves?	☐	☐	☐	☐	☐	☐
Did you feel persuaded by their arguments?	☐	☐	☐	☐	☐	☐
TOTALS	☐	☐	☐	☐	☐	☐

If you can say 'yes' to most of these, then you've just seen a very good piece of work!

RECOMMENDED READING

Dubber, Geoff
Teaching Information Skills
School Library Association, 1995
ISBN 0900641746

Dubber, Geoff
Developing Information Skills through the
Secondary School Library
School Library Association, 1999
ISBN 0900641940

Herring, James
Teaching Information Skills in Schools
Library Association, 1996
ISBN 185604176X

Lewis, Maureen & Wray, David
Writing Frames
Reading and Language Information Centre
ISBN 07049 10640

Lewis, Maureen & Wray, David
Writing Across the Curriculum
Reading and Language Information
Centre, 1998
ISBN 07049 1266X

The Library Association
Curriculum Guidance: National Curriculum
and Effective Learning

Wray, David & Lewis, Maureen
Practical Ways to Teach Reading for
Information
Reading and Language Information
Centre, 1997
ISBN 07049 10691

Publication Details

Editor: Christine A Shepherd
Advisers: Jenny Dening, Sue Hugill
Cover design: Arthur Procter
Cover photo: Superstock
Design Assistant: Debbie Maxwell
Illustrations: Craig Mitchell, Roy Mitchell
Readers: Ann Batey, Judith Wilshaw

Published by Carel Press Ltd
4 Hewson St, Carlisle CA2 5AU
Tel 01228 538928, Fax 591816
Carel_Press@compuserve.com

©2000 Claire Drury

First published: June 2000

Printed by MFP Ltd, Manchester

British Library CIP Data

Drury, Claire
Search and Discover: active library and
research skills
copiable resource
1 Library orientation for high school students
2 Information retrieval – study and teaching
  (Secondary)
I Title
025.5'678223
ISBN 1-872365-63-9

Environmental Information
The book is printed on 100% recycled paper which
is made entirely from printed waste & is not re-
bleached. Using recycled paper saves trees & water
& reduces air pollution & landfill.

ACKNOWLEDGEMENTS
Special thanks to Chris Massey and Geoff Dubber who gave me the opportunity and got me started.

Thanks also to my colleagues at Failsworth School, especially Charlie Daxon, Ruth Eversley,
Kathryn Mallea, Julie Richardson and Nigel Wickham.

Thanks also to staff at St. Aidan's Church of England High School, Harrogate, St. Joseph's Catholic
College, Bradford, Holmes Chapel Comprehensive School, Cheshire and Mike Mann, Stretford, for
sampling and commenting on the material.